GW00646432

GRESLEY PACIFICS

R.M. Tufnell

Foulis

Haynes

ISBN 0 85429 429 5

A FOULIS Railway Book

First published 1985
© **Winchmore Publishing Services Ltd 1985**

All rights reserved. No part of this book may be reproduced or transmitted in any form or by any means, electronic or mechanical, including photocopying, recording or by any information storage or retrieval system, without written permission from the publisher.

Published by:
Haynes Publishing Group
Sparkford,
Yeovil,
Somerset BA22 7JJ

Haynes Publications Inc
861 Lawrence Drive,
Newbury Park,
California 91320, USA

Produced by:
Winchmore Publishing Services Limited,
40 Triton Square,
London NW1 3HG

Printed in England

Titles in the *Super Profile* series:

BSA Bantam (F333)
MV Agusta America (F334)
Norton Commando (F335)
Honda CB750 sohc (F351)
Sunbeam S7 & S8 (F363)
BMW R69 & R69S (F387)

Austin-Healey 'Frogeye' Sprite (F343)
Ferrari 250GTO (F308)
Fiat X1/9 (F341)
Ford GT40 (F332)
Jaguar E-Type (F370)
Jaguar D-Type & XKSS (F371)
Jaguar Mk 2 Saloons (F307)
Lotus Elan (F330)
MGB (F305)

MG Midget & Austin-Healey Sprite (except 'Frogeye') (F344)
Morris Minor & 1000 (ohv) (F331)
Porsche 911 Carrera (F311)
Triumph Stag (F342)

Avro Vulcan (F436)
B-29 Superfortress (F339)
Boeing 707 (F356)
De Havilland Mosquito (F422)
Harrier (F357)
Mikoyan-Gurevich MiG 21 (F439)
P-51 Mustang (F423)
Phantom II (F376)
Sea King (F377)

SEPECAT Jaguar (F438)
Super Etendard (F378)
Tiger Moth (F421)
Bell UH-1 Iroquois (F437)

Deltics (F430)
Great Western Kings (F426)
Green Arrow (F427)
Gresley Pacifics (F429)
InterCity 125 (F428)
Royal Scot (F431)

Further titles in this series will be published at regular intervals. For information on new titles please contact your bookseller or write to the publisher.

 British Library Cataloguing in Publication Data

Gresley Pacific super profile.—(Super profile)
1. Gresley, *Sir* Nigel   2. Locomotives—
Great Britain
I. Tuffnell, R.N.   II. Series
625.2'61'0941   TJ603.4.G7

ISBN 0-85429-429-5

**Library of Congress Catalog
Card Number** 84-48-791

Contents

The Formative Years 1876-1911

Herbert Nigel Gresley (Sir Nigel from 1936) was born at Netherseale, Derbyshire on 19 June 1876 and educated at Marlborough College. He commenced his railway career at Crewe as a pupil to Francis Webb, the Chief Mechanical Engineer of the London & North Western Railway, then known as the 'Premier' line. Not content with what he could learn just at Crewe, Gresley went on to study under John Aspinall (later Sir John) at the Horwich works of the Lancashire & Yorkshire Railway. John Aspinall was probably the most forward-looking of all the Mechanical Engineers of that era, being responsible not only for some fine steam locomotives—in one of which he introduced the first attempt at superheating in the UK—but also for the pioneering of electric traction on the line between Liverpool and Southport, which was completed in nine months in 1903.

While Gresley was at Crewe it was a most interesting period in the history of the LNWR, since Francis Webb was a strong advocate of the use of the compound cycle in his locomotives. His predecessor, John Ramsbottom, had established Crewe Works as the foremost engineering establishment in the world and had instigated the system of batch production using components machined to such tolerances as to make them interchangeable. He also introduced the split cast iron piston ring which is in use in every piston engine in the world today, and in 1860 developed the use of the water trough (track pan in the USA) from which locomotive tenders could be filled at speed, thus enabling long non-

stop runs to be undertaken.

When Webb took over at Crewe in 1871, his first locomotives were similar to those of his predecessor, one of which when rebuilt in 1887 was a 2-4-0 of the 'Precedent' class with two inside cylinders and valve gear. No 790, named *Hardwicke* after the designer of the Doric portico at Euston station, was to become world famous and is still preserved today.

Webb then tried the application of compounding and after considerable trials and tribulations the 'Teutonic' class, first produced in 1889, performed sterling duty, though they were prone to difficulties in starting since the driving wheels were not coupled and could even oppose each other. These Teutonic engines were of the 2-2-2-0 wheel arrangement, with three cylinders, and had three sets of internal valve gear. Gresley would have seen these in the works and probably talked to fitters who worked on them. Even if he did not work on them himself, he would have got some idea of the problems of the assembly and setting up of the gear.

While Gresley was at Crewe, just about a year after he started, the LNWR was engaged in the great 'Race to the North' of 1895. That was a revival of the battle that had started seven years previously between the East and the West Coast lines for the Edinburgh traffic. In 1888 the best time for the journey from London to Edinburgh had been reduced to 7 hours 27 minutes, but then the competition cooled down for a while.

With the opening of the Forth Bridge in 1890, there was

renewed competition to get even further north to Aberdeen and in 1895 the West Coast Companies, that is the LNWR and the Caledonian Railway, started a speed-up. On the night of 22 August they ran the 540 miles (869 km) in 512 minutes, thus beating the East Coast competition by eight minutes. The trains were very light, only 70 tons (71.12 tonnes), and Webb's compound *Adriatic* No 1309 completed the first 158 miles (254 km) to Crewe in 147 minutes; locomotives were then changed and *Hardwicke* No 790 ran the next 141 miles (227 km) to Carlisle, including the 900 ft (274 m) climb over Shap, in 126 minutes.

Since the changeover at Crewe took place at just before half past ten in the evening, there is every chance that Gresley would have been on the platform at Crewe that evening; in fact most of the Crewe works would probably have been out to witness that event though only a few would have been allowed on that particular platform. Francis Webb himself was probably there with his top assistants and possibly some of his pupils; there would also have been the Stationmaster in his top hat and frock coat, since Crewe was a first class station.

Looking up the line in the darkening August evening they would have seen the twin lights of *Adriatic* as she came tearing down Madeley Bank at around 80 mph (129 km/h); the same Madeley Bank down which the *Coronation Scot* was to achieve 114 mph (183 km/h) in 1937, in rivalry to the achievements of Gresley's Pacifics, and so nearly come to disaster.

At half a minute after 10.27 pm the train came to a halt, having clocked just 147.5 minutes for the 158 miles (254 km), a time that was not to be improved on until 16 November 1936 when Stanier's Pacific No

The Settle & Carlisle
centenary train on
1 May 1976, headed by
LNWR Precedent
No. 790, *Hardwicke*,
and LNER No. 4472,
Flying Scotsman.

6201 swept through Crewe in 133 minutes. *Adriatic*'s driver stopped just by the changeover points and then there started a Brabham-style pit stop. *Adriatic* would be backed up to loosen the couplings and then moved sharply away over the points while the little *Hardwicke* was ready to back on to the train; a smart lift of the coupling hook onto the first carriage, tighten up the screw, and 90 seconds later they were ready to get away by 10.29 pm. The other stops on the journey at Carlisle and at Perth took three and five minutes respectively.

Forty years on, when Gresley saw the crowds at Kings Cross to witness the departure of his *Silver Jubilee*, one wonders if he remembered that evening at Crewe in 1895. He certainly could not have foreseen that 81 years later the *Hardwicke* would act as pilot to one of his Pacifics.

Another event in 1895 that probably impressed itself on Gresley's memory was when another of Webb's compounds, No 1305 *Ionic*, ran the 299 miles

(481 km) from Euston to Carlisle non-stop; that was the longest distance over which any one Company's lines permitted a non-stop run and was a world record until 27 April 1928, when Gresley's own Pacific ran non-stop from London to Edinburgh.

It can be assumed that working on the complicated valve gear of these engines, both in the shops and in the running sheds, put Gresley off the idea of having to use such a mechanism for working the valves, though it is doubtful if he could have been considering designing his own type of valve gear at that date.

Gresley left Crewe in 1898 to go on to Horwich, and here again he was to find their express locomotives had inside cylinders and valve gear. At that time the inside cylinder arrangement was favoured in the UK because the cylinders were placed under the smokebox, which made for short steam and exhaust pipes; also the cylinders formed a neat tie between the frames, whereas outside cylinders imposed a greater stress on the frames and did not look so neat

in the final appearance.

Just after Gresley arrived at Horwich, the Lancashire & Yorkshire brought out a new 'Atlantic'-style locomotive which had a 4-4-2 wheel arrangement (2-B-1), first used by the Atlantic Coast Line in the USA from which it got its nomenclature. The small trailing wheel allowed the use of a wider firebox of the Wooten type, designed by John E. Wooten of the Philadelphia & Reading Railroad in 1866 so as to enable the use of poorer quality coal.

While the L&Y were bringing out their Atlantics it was a race with the Great Northern Railway. H. A. Ivatt, GNR's Chief Mechanical Engineer, who had worked under Aspinall earlier in Ireland, just managed to produce his first Atlantic No 990 from Doncaster a few months ahead of the 'Lanky' version.

It was these GNR Atlantics, together with their larger version produced in 1902, that Gresley was to take over from H. A. Ivatt as the first line locomotives of the GNR when he himself took over in 1911.

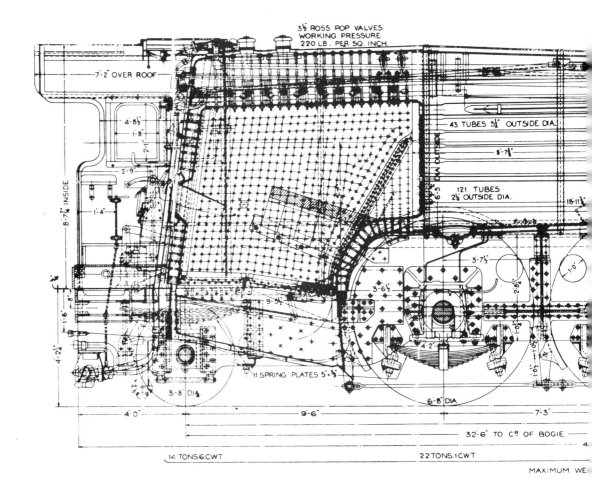

3½ ROSS POP VALVES
WORKING PRESSURE.
220 LB. PER SQ. INCH

7'-2" OVER ROOF

43 TUBES 5¼" OUTSIDE DIA.

8'-7½"

121 TUBES
2½" OUTSIDE DIA.

18'-11¼"

4'-8½"
1'-8"
2'-1"

2'-9"

8'-7½" INSIDE

1'-4"

3'-7½"

3'-6½"

9'-5½"

1'-0"

2'-8½"

1'-6"

4'-2½"

4'-2"

11 SPRING PLATES 5'×⅝"

3'-8" DIA

6'-8" DIA.

4'-0"

9'-6"

7'-3"

32'-6" TO C⅊ OF BOGIE

14 TONS.6.CWT

22 TONS.1.CWT

MAXIMUM WE

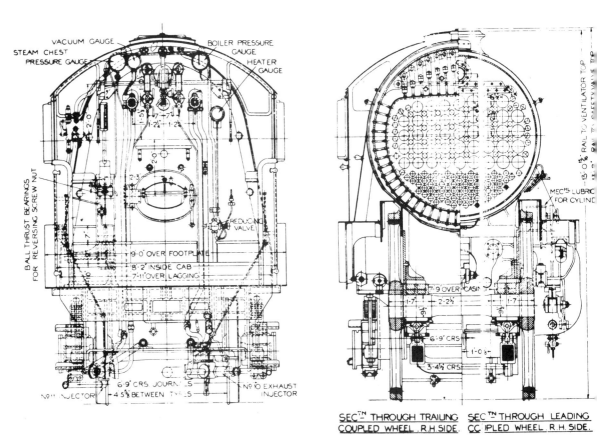

VACUUM GAUGE
STEAM CHEST
PRESSURE GAUGE

BOILER PRESSURE
GAUGE
HEATER
GAUGE

BALL THRUST BEARINGS
FOR REVERSING SCREW NUT

REDUCING
VALVE

9'-0" OVER FOOTPLATE
8'-2" INSIDE CAB
7'-11" OVER LAGGING

6'-9" CRS JOURN'LS
4'-5¾" BETWEEN TYRES

Nº 11 INJECTOR

Nº 10 EXHAUST
INJECTOR

13'-0"⅞ RAIL TO VENTILATOR TOP

MECH⅃ LUBRIC
FOR CYLIND

7'-9" OVER CASIN

1'-7"
2'-2½"
1'-7"

6'-9" CRS

1'-0⅞"

3'-4½" CRS

SEC TN THROUGH TRAILING
COUPLED WHEEL. R.H. SIDE.

SEC TN THROUGH LEADING
CC UPLED WHEEL. R.H. SIDE.

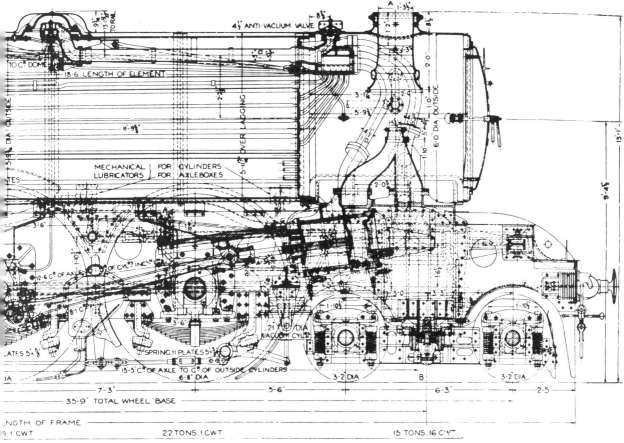

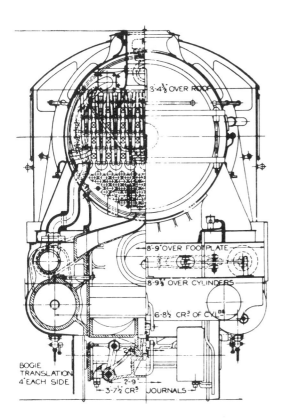

Weight diagram of 'K-3' 2-6-0, built from 1921. The first Mogul of Gresley design with the three-cylinder valve gear.

Great Northern 1911-1922

Apart from a summer season's spell in the locomotive running shed at Blackpool in 1901, Gresley was to devote the next 10 years on the Carriage & Wagon side of the railway business. That short time in Blackpool would have been very active, since it was quite common for 300,000 people to be transported to and from that seaside resort on a single summer's day. Blackpool is also well known for its romantic associations and Gresley's wife, whom he married in 1901, came from nearby St Anne's-on-Sea. In that year also he went to the carriage works at Newton Heath and three years later became Assistant Superintendent of the C & W Department. That appointment was to last for only one year and in 1905 he obtained a similar post on the Great Northern Railway at Doncaster.

The Great Northern Railway, next to the London & North Western, was the most prestigious line to run north out of London and the GNR had been running the 'Flying Scotsman' in conjunction with the North Eastern and the North British Railways since 1862, though not always under that name, since it was first known as the 'Special Scotch Express'. On the carriage side they had introduced dining cars in 1879, corridors in 1881 and buckeye couplers combined with Pullman-type vestibules in 1896.

The GNR works at Doncaster, known as 'The Plant', was opened in 1853 with 900 employees, which by 1900 had grown to 4,500. At the Carriage & Wagon works the predominant style for main line stock had been with the clerestory roof, a relic of the days when roof ventilation was needed because of the use of gas for carriage lighting. One of Gresley's first objects in carriage design was to eliminate the use of gas in passenger cars because of the risk of fire, which was particularly prevalent in the event of a derailment or collision.

The first products from the C&W works which carried Gresley's design work were two steam rail motor cars built in 1905, in which a steam-powered bogie unit was coupled to a new style coach with an elliptical roof. The power unit, which was significant, was equipped with two outside cylinders 10 in (25.4 cm) by 16 in (40.5 cm) for which the valve gear was driven by an external Walschaerts mechanism, the first time this was ever used by the GNR. It obviously made a great impression on Gresley since he was to use that in nearly all his own locomotive designs. It would have been much easier to adjust and maintain than the inside type of gear that he had been used to.

Those railcars were rather underpowered, but lasted until 1925 when they were rebuilt as ordinary coaches.

Some of Gresley's other achievements during his time in the C & W Department were to make a profound impression on the Directors of the GNR. They included first a prototype bogie luggage van No 126 for the East Coast Joint Stock which was the first vehicle to be built at Doncaster with an all-steel underframe; the bodysides were of teak, which became the standard finish for the future LNER main line stock including the Flying Scotsman. That coach was produced in 1906, as were some new cars for the Manchester Fliers which had 'Great Northern' in large gilt letters on their bodysides.

In 1907 Gresley introduced some articulated coaches for both suburban and main line use which were an innovation in the UK, and this form of construction was to be used later in his high speed trains as a means of saving weight. He also produced some close-coupled double-brake vans which allowed the weight of freight trains to be increased to 600 tons (609.6 tonnes) and which later induced him to increase the output from his freight locomotives and to adopt the three-cylinder design.

In 1908 Doncaster produced a new Royal Train consisting of six vehicles with an extra car for

Weight diagram of 1902 Ivatt 'Atlantic'.

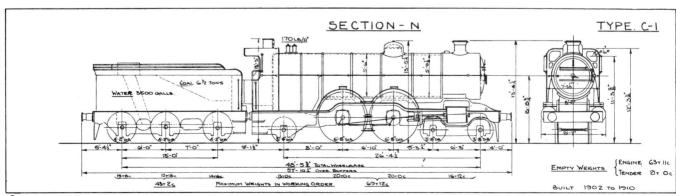

Queen Alexandra. It made its first journey on 7 September 1908 from Kings Cross to Ollerton and on that occasion Gresley himself rode in the train to make sure all was satisfactory. The last item of note in the C&W story also took place in 1908 when Gresley adopted as a standard bogie one that had been produced by Spencer, Moulton & Co. It had a double bolster springborne in the bogie frame and carried a third central bolster which itself carried the pivot point of the coach body. These bogies became what was to be known as the standard LNER Gresley bogie and were nearly adopted as the standard for British Railways after nationalisation in 1948.

In 1911 H. A. Ivatt retired and at the age of thirty-five Gresley was appointed as the Loco-motive, Carriage & Wagon Superintendent of the Great Northern Railway thus taking on the responsibility for the provision of all the stock and the necessary motive power to keep the railway operational. He also thus qualified for the Member-ship of the Association of Rail-way Locomotive Engineers and in that forum he would have interchanged ideas with such well-known locomotive designers as C. J. Bowen-Cooke of the LNWR; George Jackson Church-ward of the GWR; Dugald Drummond of the London & South Western; Henry Fowler of the Midland and Vincent Raven of the North Eastern. Also in later years his locomotives would be destined to run over the lines for which those Mechanical Engineers were responsible and long after they had all retired.

When Gresley took over in 1911, the most powerful pas-senger locomotives on the GNR were the large boilered Atlantics that Ivatt had first produced in 1902 and which lasted for

twenty years in that category. At first they had barely been capable of handling their trains, but from 1910, when they were fitted with superheaters, they became capable of the most fantastic feats of haulage for their size.

The application of super-heating, by which the steam was given an extra pass through the heat from the firebox, was as big a breakthrough as James Watt's application of the separate condenser. The performance of many locomotives, including Churchward's famous 'Saints' and 'Stars', was revolutionised by this simple device that cost so little to fit, probably not much more then than about £100 per boiler. It has incidentally made possible the modern power station boiler, by means of which efficiencies as high as 40 per cent can be achieved. At the time that superheating was applied to the steam locomotive there were no steam tables available from which designers could calculate what they were getting in the form of heat value. All they knew was that the efficiency of the steam engine was doubled overnight.

While Gresley was doing his sterling work in the Carriage & Wagon Department, his chief, H. A. Ivatt, was testing out the

application of superheating, first to an 0-8-0 No 417 in 1908 and then to one of his earlier Atlantics, No 989. In 1910, ten of the new Atlantics, Nos 1452 to 1461, were produced at 'The Plant', fitted with superheaters as new.

All this work would have been closely studied by Gresley and discussed in the Mess at Doncaster with his chief and with other operating executives of the GNR. 'Shop' talk was not barred in railway messes, as it is supposed to be in Regimental ones, and that discussion would no doubt have ranged over what other lines were doing, particu-larly the 'Saints' and 'Stars' of the Great Western and the new 'Precursor' class which Crewe were producing at the rate of two per week. That rate was typical of a main works at that time, but pales into insignificance beside General Motors' production of 10 a day some 50 years later.

Ivatt was so impressed with the Crewe product that he persuaded the LNWR to arrange an exchange of locomotives for trial. He is reputed to have ridden on the footplate of the Precursor No 412 *Marquis* and to have offered the North Western crew a pair of new hats if they could beat the time of 18 minutes to the top of the climb at Potters

Ivatt 'Atlantic' No. 3296 on down Express near Hatfield in Superheated form and in LNER livery.

Bar, 12.5 miles (20 km) from Kings Cross.

If H. A. Ivatt was of a similar nature to his equally famous son H. G. Ivatt, who produced the first main line diesel locomotive No 10000, he would have had a considerable sense of humour and been a delightful person to work for. There is a long link through the Ivatt family between the first British Atlantic No 990 and the many class 31 diesel-electrics first delivered to the Eastern Region of British Railways in 1957, since H.G.'s influence in the design of D5500 (the first of the class 31) was considerable. It was a fitting tribute that one of the last of the Eastern Region Pacifics, No 60123, was named *H. A. Ivatt*.

Among the locomotives that Gresley inherited on his takeover in 1911 was a deficiency in the range of units capable of handling mixed traffic—that is, medium speed passenger trains and fast freight trains in which enough vehicles were fitted with brakes to enable them to run at up to 60 mph (96 km/h). In 1910 H. Holcroft of the GWR had paid a visit to Canada and found that locomotives of the 2-6-0 wheel arrangement, called 'Moguls', were performing that duty very successfully; the GWR designed and built some of these for service in 1911. They didn't waste time in getting in on new ideas in those days and Gresley was quick to follow suit. His first 2-6-0, No 1630 (later 61720), came out as his maiden design in 1912. That model followed Ivatt's pattern in general but was novel in the use of Walschaerts valve gear, and the guiding pony wheel was carried in a truck

having double swing links. Nine more were built the following year and these were later classified as K.1 in the LNER system. In 1912 two other events of interest occurred at Doncaster in that Gresley selected as his assistant one O. V. S. Bulleid, a former Doncaster pupil and, to succeed Gresley in the C & W Department, the Directors chose Edward Thompson from the North Eastern, who himself was to take over from Gresley in 1941.

The outbreak of war in 1914 caused a major upheaval in the administration of the UK railway system since it was all brought under the control of the Government, but administered by a Committee of General Managers. That Committee had been set up in 1912 in preparation for war, but was not prepared for the tremendous load of munitions production that was imposed on the locomotive workshops. In order to meet that demand, most of the locomotive work of the GNR was moved to the shops of the former Midland & Great Northern Railway at Melton Constable and Doncaster was largely turned over to producing the sinews of war.

Increasing train loads due to wartime demands prompted

A 2-8-0 of the 'O' Class. The first to be fitted with the Gresley three-cylinder conjugated valve gear.

Gresley into the use of more than two cylinders in order to obtain the power output required. The first application of this idea in 1915 was to equip one of the Ivatt Atlantics, No 279 (62808), with four cylinders 15 in (38 cm) by 24 in (61 cm), but that particular modification was not very successful and needed more maintenance than the standard two-cylinder version. For No 279 the valve gear for the inside cylinders was driven by rocker arms from the outside gear, which was worked by Walschaerts gear. That was the exact opposite to the system for the four-cylinder engines on the GWR, but Gresley seems to have been determined not to use inside valve gear at any price, no doubt from personal experience.

After the four-cylinder arrangement was found not to be the answer, the next logical step was to use three cylinders. This had the advantage of producing a more even torque with six thrusts per revolution of the wheels as against four for either two or four cylinders. Actually with four cylinders it is possible to obtain eight thrusts per revolution, as was done on the Southern Railways' 'Lord Nelson', but there is a disadvantage in that too even a torque does not produce enough blast to keep an adequate fire in the firebox.

The locomotive boiler was unique in that it relied on the pulsations from the chimney to

keep the firebed in motion, so that it was akin to a white-hot beating heart. The ordinary open fire in a living room is about one square foot in area, whereas the firegrate of a large locomotive is some 40 times that area. Imagine an area eight feet by five, stacked to a depth of 12 or 15 inches of coal glowing white hot at a temperature of 3,000 °F and having to be fed by a shovel from one end at the rate of 50 lb (23 kg) a minute. That coal must be evenly spread over the whole fire and all through a hole only just large enough to take the shovel with its load of coal. That gives some idea of the skill required of a fireman in a steam locomotive.

It was found that if the blast was too even the fire would not draw, and that was one of the reasons why the various turbine locomotives were not successful. By 1916 enough three-cylinder locomotives were in use to prove that they could be successful, so Gresley's next problem was to devise a valve gear that would operate an internal cylinder from an external drive arrangement.

The valve gear on a steam locomotive is unlike that on any other form of steam engine in that it has to be capable of producing a large thrust at low speed by the maximum opening of the valves, and then taper off the steam supply as the speed increases; that is achieved by varying the stroke of the valve which the driver controls through his reversing screw mechanism. This variation in cut-off was usually from 75 per cent in full gear to around 15 per cent. It

was never run in neutral since some form of cushion had to be provided to prevent the pistons hitting the ends of the cylinder.

A further advantage of the three-cylinder arrangement was that it was impossible to get stuck on a 'dead centre'. With two or even four cylinders, a locomotive could be brought to a halt with all pistons in the mid-cylinder position and, in that unlucky event, it took quite a bit of juggling with the valve gear to get an engine moving again. For two years Gresley worked on the valve gear problem although pressure of other war work no doubt held this up since he also served on the Engineering Committee of the Ministry of Food, for which work he was awarded the CBE.

In 1918 Gresley was at last able to produce his first three-cylinder locomotive. This was a 2-8-0 (1D) freight engine No 461 (later renumbered 3461, then 3921 and finally 63921) originally with cylinders 18 in (46 cm) by 26 in (66 cm) and in which the valves for the inside cylinder were operated by a conjugated system of linkage from the outside cylinder valve gear. To operate these, a vertical screw reversing gear was adopted, similar to that in use on the Horwich-built locomotives when Gresley was there, and was a great success. No 461 could handle freight trains of up to 1,300 tons, some 200 tons more than the two-cylinder version and had better coal consumption, being 4.76 lb per hp against that of 5.19 for the two-cylinder type.

The Gresley Pacific design of 1915, based on an elongated Ivatt Atlantic but never built.

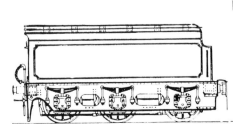

The next step was the production in 1920 of an improved Mogul 2-6-0 class, having three cylinders 18.5 in (47 cm) diameter by 26 in (66 cm) stroke with a steam pressure of 180 lb per sq in and driving wheels of 68 in (173 cm) diameter. The first of that class was No 1000 (later 4000, then 1800 and 61800) and one of its outstanding features was its large boiler, which had a diameter of six feet (1.8 m) and a phenomenal steaming capacity. These 1000 class locomotives, later known as K.3, were capable of handling all types of fast freight trains and in passenger service could equal the performance of the Ivatt Atlantics, being capable of running at up to 75 mph (120 km/h). At that speed their driving wheels would have been revolving at 371 rpm, not fast by modern standards but quite enough for steel wheels the size of a man and weighing nearly two tons (2.032 tonnes) each.

Having established the success of his aim at producing good three-cylinder locomotives without having to resort to internal valve gears, Gresley's next logical step was to produce a more powerful express passenger unit than the large Ivatt Atlantics, which had carried the bulk of the express trains since their

inception in 1902. Here again he was faced with the problem of which wheel arrangement to adopt. Most of the other railways in the UK chose to use the 4-6-0 wheel arrangement since that gave the maximum adhesion per ton of locomotive, assuming that a bogie is essential for high speed running, but that arrangement entailed a narrow firebox that could fit in between the last pair of coupled wheels.

The lines forming the East Coast route had traditionally relied on the supply of Yorkshire coal, which was not of a high calorific value and needed a large firebox to ensure adequate combustion. The only other wheel arrangement which would allow the continued use of that fuel was the 4-6-2 (2C1) or Pacific type, first used by the Missouri Pacific RR in 1902; by 1921 it was in widespread use in the USA as well as in Europe and many other parts of the world. Until then only one, *The Great Bear* No 111, had been built in the UK (by the GWR in 1908) and had not been a success story; it was overweight for most of the GWR system and did not steam as well as their 'Star' class 4-6-0 locomotives.

By 1921 an Act of Parliament had laid down the basis for the reorganisation of Britain's

No. 1470. The first A.1 Gresley Pacific, *Great Northern*, built in 1922 just prior to the Amalgamation.

railways into four groups, which was due to be implemented by 1923. Gresley knew that he must get his new locomotive out before then, rather as H. G. Ivatt produced his first diesel-electric mainliner, No 10000, in 1947 just in time to get the letters LMS on the side before nationalisation. He also must have known that his next door neighbours, the North Eastern Railway, were about to produce a Pacific and that both models would be in competition in the same group after the amalgamation.

Back in 1915 Gresley had produced a design for a Pacific based on a stretched Ivatt Atlantic, rather as the *Great Bear* and Raven's Pacific were, and that 1915 design was based on four cylinders similar to the rebuilt Atlantic No 279. Fortunately it was not produced, possibly due to the pressure of war work at Doncaster and possibly due to the poor results obtained from No 279 itself; whatever the reasons, it would never have been as effective as the actual model produced in April 1922 from 'The Plant' at Doncaster, No 1470 called *Great Northern*.

The A1 Pacifics 1922-1928

A headmaster's report on these first Pacifics might have read, 'Fine effort, but could do better.' Certainly when No 1470 made its first appearance in April 1922 the effect was striking and heralded a new phase of British steam locomotive history. The huge boiler, 77 in (196 cm) diameter at the firebox end with a barrel length of 19 ft (5.8 m), gave an impression of power that was way ahead of any other engine then in service on the railway systems of the UK. The firegrate area of 41.25 sq ft (12.6 sq m) was also larger than any other standard British locomotive and had only been exceeded by unique types such as Holden's *Decapod*, which was 42 sq ft (12.8 sq m), the Midland *Paget* with its brick-lined firebox of 55 sq ft (16.8 sq m) and *The Great Bear* with 41.8 sq ft (12.8 sq m).

One of the objects in producing this Pacific locomotive had been to cope with passenger trains of up to 600 tons (609.6 tonnes) in weight. That demand had arisen during the war of 1914/18 and during the three months coal strike of 1921, when trains of 500 tons (508 tonnes) and more had to be handled by the large Ivatt Atlantics or the '1000' class 2-6-0 Moguls. In June 1921 an 18-coach train of

605 tons (614,718 kg) was worked from Doncaster to Peterborough by 2-6-0 No 1006 and from Peterborough to London by No 1007. Average speeds were nearly 50 mph (80 km/h) with a recorded maximum speed of 76 mph (122 km/h); the overall coal consumption was 51 lb (23 kg) per mile.

At that time (1922) train speeds were on the low side and most trains were much slower than they had been in 1914. The war and the threat of the 'Amalgamation' had a stultifying effect, just as happened after the 1939/45 war with the threat of Nationalisation hanging over everyone in the railway industry. Train times to places like York and Newcastle-upon-Tyne were nearly 30 minutes longer than in 1914, and the longest non-stop run on the Great Northern was only 105 miles (170 km) from Kings Cross to Grantham. In the speed table they were lying ninth out of 14 main lines with a fastest train at only 54 mph (87 km/h) for the 50.5 miles (81 km) from Grantham to Doncaster. In order to handle a 600-ton (609,638-kg) train at 60 mph (96.5 km/h) the train resistance is around 10 lb (46 kg) per ton, so that a drawbar pull of 6,000 lb (2,721 kg) is required which would imply a starting tractive effort of almost 30,000 lb

(13,608 kg); for No 1470 this was quoted as 29,835 lb (13,533 kg). When Churchward was designing his express locomotive at Swindon in 1902, his aim was to achieve a drawbar pull of 2 tons (2.032 tonnes) at 70 mph (112 km/h) which was aimed at hauling a 350-ton (355.6 tonnes) train at that speed. In order to haul a 600-ton (609.6-tonnes) train at 70 mph (112 km/h) the pull would need to be 3.2 tons (3.25 tonnes) which was probably beyond the capacity of Gresley's first Pacific, but trains of that weight were not expected to run at such speeds.

When the first two Pacifics, Nos 1470 and 1471, were built, they cost £12,350 each including the tender, which compared with a cost of £5,260 for the Swindon Pacific *The Great Bear*, built in 1907. However the relative cost-of-living index in 1922 was just twice that of 1907 and the cost of the Great Northern Pacifics included all the design and development charges, so that the cost of the next batch was only £7,614 each.

Meantime, the North Eastern Railway had not been idle and in July 1922 had published all the plans of a Pacific locomotive under construction at their works at Darlington. That was completed in December 1922, just ahead of the amalgamation, and so carried the North Eastern insignia on its first model No 2400, though it did not at that time have a name. Some tech-

Weight diagram of 1922 A.1 Pacific.

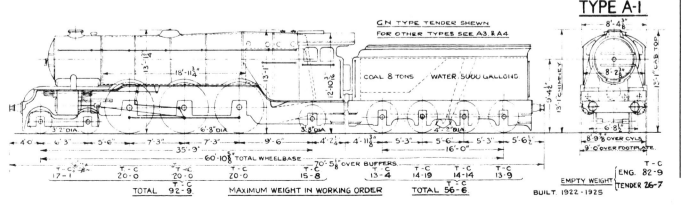

The rival Pacific. Sir Vincent Raven's design No. 2400 of the North Eastern Railway, built in 1922 in NER livery.

nical details of that engine are shown alongside those for No 1470 and *The Great Bear* in the specifications at the end of this book.

All this must have been of some concern to Gresley, who would have been wondering which of the Mechanical Engineers from the four principal railways due to form the London & North Eastern Group would get the top job. Since his Pacifics were some months ahead in production, they were able to get some trial running during the summer of 1922, when a few drivers and firemen could get the chance to learn how to handle them before they were asked to do any really heavy duties.

A steam locomotive could look very fine when newly emerged from the works, but it was that subtle combination of the fireman's shovel and the driver's use of his regulator and reversing gear that would prove whether it was any good in the long run. The fireman had to keep his fire even and yet not too hot or it would clinker; the boiler had to steam well and not run short just when it was needed for a stiff climb, and the steam had to get into and out of the cylinders at the right speed. For the latter function the operation of the valve gear was critical; if the combination of exhaust outlet and blast pipe were not correct, the boiler would not steam properly and the back pressure on

the exhaust side could cause sluggish running, with reduced overall efficiency. That again would affect the coal and water consumption and make the fireman's job still more difficult.

After the initial running-in and training, Nos 1470 and 1471 were put to work the 5.40 pm Leeds express down from Kings Cross, which was the hardest working at that time. They were able to improve on the 87-minute schedule to Peterborough with train loads up to 525 tons (533.4 tonnes), at least 100 tons (101.6 tonnes) more than the Atlantics could handle.

Gresley had claimed that these locomotives were designed to handle 600-ton (609.6 tonnes) trains and No 1471 proved this by hauling a 617-ton (626.9 tonnes) train from London to Grantham at an average speed of 51.8 mph (83 km/h). But the coal consumption on these heavy duties was enormous. According to drivers' reports, they could consume a tender-load of coal, almost eight tons (8.12 tonnes), on a run from Grantham to Kings Cross and back, equivalent to nearly 80 lb (36 kg) per mile. Incidentally, that would have included a run from Kings Cross to Hornsey and back to turn round, using the triangle at Hornsey since they were too long to use the turntable then installed at Kings Cross.

The reason for the high coal consumption was basically in the

valve gear, since the length of travel of the piston valves was only 4.56 in (11.5 cm) and the diameter just 8 in (20 cm). The valves on the very successful 1000 class Moguls had a travel of 6.38 in (16 cm) and a diameter of 8 in (20 cm) for a smaller cylinder size, and those engines had proved themselves capable of working 600-ton trains as well as of high speed running. The limitation in the valve gear of the original Pacifics was apparently imposed by the layout at the front end, which limited the length of the combination lever that worked the valve rod. This was described as like tying together the legs of a fast horse and must have been a worry and a disappointment to Gresley. However, this aspect did not at first appear too serious and the Directors approved the building of a further ten of these Pacifics before the end of 1922.

The Railways Act of 1921 was given the Royal Assent on 19 August of that year and the resulting 'Amalgamation' took place on 1 January 1923. That was a most traumatic event in the lives of most of the railway senior management since out of fourteen principal railways there would be only four top jobs to be filled. Only on the Great Western Railway would there be no problems since that line remained virtually intact, as it had been pre-war. The London Midland & Scottish Railway, with a capital of over £400 million, was probably the largest private commercial concern in the world; the London & North Eastern Railway was the second largest of the 'Big Four', as they were known, and had a capital of £348 million. Its main constituent railways were the North Eastern (1,758 miles/2,829 km), North British (1,378 miles/2,217 km),

Great Eastern (1,191 miles/
1,916 km), Great Northern
(1,051 miles/1,691 km) and the
Great Central (852 miles/1,371
km), as well as many smaller
companies. The total rolling
stock consisted of 7,383 locomotives (in 236 classes), 20,156
coaches and 300,464 freight
vehicles.

The North Eastern was the
dominant line in the Group and
the most profitable, but they all
showed a return on their capital
of around four per cent. There
was a lot of duplication with the
LMS Railway since both systems
provided services to Rugby,
Leicester, Nottingham, Sheffield,
Manchester and Leeds, as well as
to Edinburgh and Glasgow,
which was to influence the
future LNER locomotive policy.
In Scotland the overlapping was
chronic, owing to the old feud
between the Highland Railway
and the Great North of Scotland
in which neither would agree to
go into the same group as the
other. These points are shown on
the two system maps which were
issued in their advertisements in
1923.

At the time of the grouping,
each of the Big Four had one
named train only, apart from
some Pullman trains which
carried their destination towns as
names. The Southern Railway
had their 'Southern Belle', which
was a Pullman train running the
52 miles (84 km) to Brighton in
the hour, steam-hauled then as it
was to be for the next ten years.
The Great Western had their
'Cornish Riviera', running the
world's longest non-stop run of
225.7 miles (363 km) to
Plymouth. The LMS had their
'Irish Mail', the oldest named
train in the world, which had
borne its title since 1848; it was
not a fast train but a real watch-
setter, and had been the crack
train of the former LNWR when
Dublin was the second most

important city in the British Isles.
The LNER had their 'Flying
Scotsman', originally named in
1862 as the 'Special Scotch
Express', but unofficially described since 1893 as the 'Flying
Scotsman'. 'Crawling' would
have been a more suitable name
than 'Flying', since it went about
as fast as a Scotsman on the day
after Hogmanay, but it was
extremely comfortable. Some of
the first class compartments had
only two seats each side, as
befitted a worthy citizen of some
substance; for a fare of over £4
to Edinburgh, which in those
days was a lot more than most
people earned in a week, one
would expect a journey of $8\frac{1}{2}$
hours to be comfortable.

On the formation of the LNER,
the post of Mechanical Engineer
was offered first to J. G. Robin-
son of the Great Central. He was
the most senior engineer of the
constituent companies but as he
was almost due for retirement he
declined and reputedly advised
that Gresley be chosen for the
job. That was, of course, a considerable blow to Sir Vincent
Raven of the North Eastern, who
had done a fine job for that line
in the locomotive field; he had
also pioneered some electrifica-
tion work in the Tyneside area
and at Shildon, but in those days
that might not have counted in

his favour. Raven was offered a
position as a Consultant, but
after a year he left for Australia.
Gresley was safely settled in as
Chief Mechanical Engineer and
had the formidable task of trying
to get the best out of the various
locomotives and rolling stock of
the seven companies which
formed the LNER.

One of the first points to be
settled was which of the two
types of Pacific locomotive was
the most suitable for adoption as
the future standard. Since the
North Eastern had a dynamometer car of their own build, it
became available for trials of this
nature. The North Eastern
Pacific was very similar in
dimension to No 1470, having
three cylinders, but its boiler
pressure was higher by 20 lb per
sq in (at 200 lb per sq in) and all
three cylinders drove onto the
front coupled axle, having three
sets of internal valve gear. In
some ways, driving onto the
front axle was an advantage in
that all three cylinders could be
in the same line, whereas on No
1470 the inner cylinder had to be
at a higher level and inclined, so
that the connecting rod cleared
the leading coupled axle. The
disadvantage of driving onto the
leading axle was that it imposed
more severe loadings on the
mechanism when the leading

Three-cylinder block for the Pacific.

15

The built-up crank axle for the Gresley Pacifics, showing system of assembly.

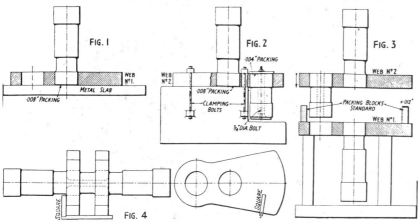

FIG. I
WEB N°1.
METAL SLAB
·008"PACKING

FIG. 2
WEB N°2.
·004"PACKING
·008"PACKING
CLAMPING BOLTS
¾"DIA.BOLT

FIG. 3
WEB N°2
PACKING BLOCKS STANDARD +·012"
WEB N°1.

FIG. 4
SQUARE
SQUARE

wheels entered a sharp curve and the axle would have to have been more elaborate than that of the GN Pacific's since it had to have not only a main crankthrow, but also three sets of eccentrics to operate the valve gears. The driving axle on the Gresley Pacific was extremely simple, having only the one centre crankthrow, and was constructed on the built-up principle rather than being forged. That system of construction was used on the crankshafts of large diesel engines at that time and consisted of heating the crankwebs, inserting the pins and letting them cool.

With a three-cylinder locomotive it was desirable to impose the drive from all cylinders onto one axle, since this eliminated all the hammer blow or vertical loading from the track. This enabled higher axle loads to be acceptable to the Civil Engineer and also gave greater adhesion for the application of power. The axle load on the North Eastern Pacific No 2400 was 20 tons (20.32 tonnes), as was that for No 1470, giving a total of 60 tons (60.96 tonnes) for adhesion. The boiler of No 2400 was more conventional, being only 6 ft (1.8 m) in diameter and, with its long parallel design, was not so impressive as the Great Northern product. By the end of 1922 only one Pacific had been produced from Darlington so there was not a lot of time for the crews to learn how to handle that type

before the comparative trials which took place in June and July 1923. In those tests No 2400 gave a good performance in the handling of heavy trains, which included the 5.40 pm ex-Kings Cross, usually well over 500 tons (508 tonnes), but in the overall results the coal consumption of the Gresley Pacific No 1472 was 48.6 lb (22 kg) per mile against that of 54.4 lb (25 kg) per mile for No 2400.

These results decided in favour of the Doncaster version, but since the second Raven Pacific had been produced at Darlington and the material for three more had been ordered, it was decided to complete all five, which were given the classification A.2. In sorting out the 236 classes of locomotives which the LNER absorbed, a new classification system was adopted. Based on wheel arrangement, it worked out as follows:

Class A	4-6-2	O	2-8-0
B	4-6-0	P	2-8-2
C	4-4-2	Q	0-8-0
D	4-4-0	R	0-8-2
E	2-4-0	S	0-8-4
F	2-4-2	T	4-8-0
G	0-4-4	U	2-8-8-2
J	0-6-0	V	2-6-2
K	2-6-0	W	4-6-4
L	2-6-4	Y	0-4-0
N	0-6-2		

This system applied whether the engine was of the tender or the tank type. The Gresley Pacific thus became A.1 and the Raven Pacific A.2.

During 1923 the second batch of 10 A.1s came out from Doncaster, starting with No 1472 in February and finishing with No 1481 in August. These all carried the numbers of the former GNR system, but with the L&NER insignia on the tenders. None of them carried names at that time since it had not been the GNR practice to name engines and the only ones named to that date had been the first Atlantic No 990, called *Henry Oakley*, and No 1470 itself. Before long the

The *Flying Scotsman* No. 4472 arriving at Chinley Station.

Above: No. 4498 on Dick Turpin Railtour to Leeds.

Left: No. 60010 (4489) *Dominion of Canada* at its present location in the Canadian Railway Museum at St. Constant, Quebec, Canada.

Above: Paperweight Model of locomotive No. 2509, 'Silver Link'.

These paperweights were produced by the LNER in September 1935 to commemorate the inauguration of the Silver Jubilee service between London and Newcastle.

Below: A4 2509 *Silver Link* in silver livery with black smokebox on Up 'Flying Scotsman' at Grantham Station.

Above: No. 60088 (2599) *Book Law* with Kylchap Exhaust on up Thames-Clyde Express near Hellifield.

Below: No. 60067 (2566) A North British-built A.1 *Ladas* rebuilt as A.3 with Kylchap Exhaust, at Kings Cross in 1959. A Baby Deltic Class 23 is also visible.

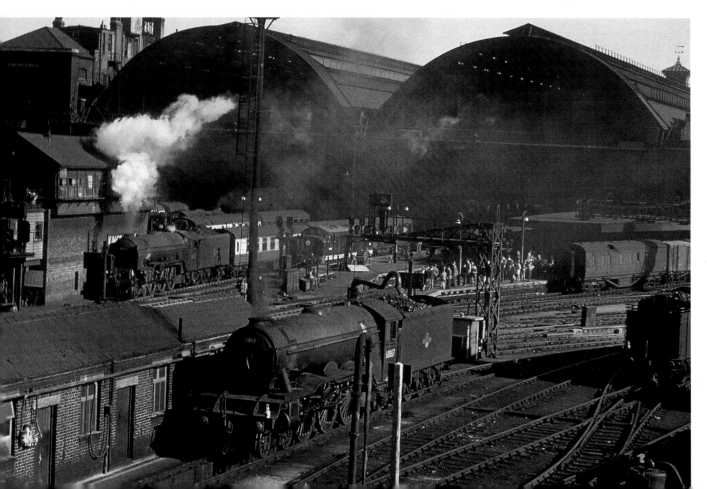

Above: No. 60067 (2566) with small smoke deflectors on down White Rose Express near Hadley Wood, April 1962.

Below: A.4s at Kings Cross Shed in 1962. Nos. 60008 (4496) *Dwight D. Eisenhower* and 60013 (4492) *Dominion of New Zealand* with open front ends.

Above: Mallard with dynamometer car and special train on 3 July, 1938.

Below: Locomotive *Sir Nigel Gresley* at the opening of the Locomotive Testing Plant at Rugby in 1948.

Right: No. 60102 *Sir Frederick Banbury,* originally No. 1471, the second Gresley Pacific. Rebuilt as A.3 on local train at Rugby on the former Great Central line.

Below: A.4 60009 (4488) *Union of South Africa* at Kings Cross in 1961.

Above: No. 60052 (2551), a 1924 A.1. rebuilt as A.3 with Kylchap Exhaust and smoke deflectors on a freight train on Waverley Route in 1963, *Prince Palatine*.

Below: Spadina Roundhouse at Toronto, visited by *Flying Scotsman* in 1970, seen from Toronto Tower.

A comparable American Pacific locomotive of 1923.

tender lettering became LNER and the numbers of former GNR locomotives had 3000 added, so that the first twelve became Nos 4470 to 4481. Names then began to be applied and in 1924 No 4472, called *Flying Scotsman*, was made ready for showing at the Empire Exhibition at Wembley; there it was sited alongside the new GWR 4-6-0 No 4073 called *Caerphilly Castle*, which had just come out of Swindon works. It was claimed as the most powerful passenger locomotive in the UK, based on a tractive effort of 31,625 lb (14,345 kg) from its four cylinders.

By way of contrast the K.3Q Pacifics built for the New York Central RR in 1923, with 79-in (200-cm) driving wheels, produced a tractive effort of 31,000 lb (14,061 kg) from only two 23-in (58-cm) diameter cylinders and the class S.292, also built in 1923 by the American Locomotive Company (ALCO) for the Chicago & Northwestern RR, gave a tractive effort of 45,000 lb (20,412 kg) from two 26-in (66-cm) diameter cylinders when fitted with 75-in (190.5-cm) diameter driving wheels. It was said that the boiler of No 1470 had been based on that of a K-4 Pacific built for the Pennsylvania Railroad in 1911, in which the design tapered from the firebox tube plate both towards the cab and towards the smokebox end.

The design for that boiler had been received at Doncaster in 1916, rather as the design on which the Swindon tapered boilers was based had come to the GWR in 1902 from the USA.

Arising out of the display at Wembley of the two most powerful steam locomotives in England, there apparently came a challenge or bet between the Chairmen of the respective companies to prove which was the better of their two products. This resulted in the interchange trials which took place in April and May of 1925. For that event the LNER approach appears to have been a bit slapdash, almost as if it wasn't taken seriously, but the GWR effort was thorough and completely organised, similar to the Mercedes-Benz approach to a Grand Prix event. The two GWR 'Castles' detailed for the trials were beautifully turned out and prepared, as befitted the products of Swindon whose manufacturing methods were more scientifically advanced than any other railway workshop. Their crews also had an *esprit de corps* which had not lessened as a result of the 1923 amalgamation, which the other conglomerates were still suffering from.

The visiting Pacific on the route to Plymouth was No 4474, *Victor Wild*, and it put up a very reasonable performance on a route not really suitable for such a long engine; it adhered rigidly to schedule, whereas the GWR competitor, No 4074 *Caldicote*

Castle, put on some startling performances with arrivals up to 15 minutes ahead of time. On the East Coast route between Kings Cross and Doncaster, the LNER twice suffered from mechanical troubles and the engine finally selected for the trials, No 2545 *Diamond Jubilee*, did not do justice to her class. Again, the Castle sent out by Swindon, No 4079 *Pendennis Castle*, put in some unexpected results, even running well on the supposedly low-calorific Yorkshire coal. It started 475-ton (482.6 tonnes) trains out of Kings Cross without a trace of slipping, due to the excellent design of the GWR type of steam regulator and once even reached Potters Bar in the 18-minute time that Ivatt had asked of his visitor from the LNWR back in 1909.

The overall results of these trials had showed that the Castle performance was as good if not better than that of the larger Pacific and that it was much more economical in fuel. The coal consumption between London and Doncaster was 55.3 lb (25 kg) per mile for the Pacific and 49.7 lb (22.5 kg) per mile for the Castle, while between London and Plymouth the figures were 50.4 lb (22.9 kg) and 48.8 lb (22 kg) respectively.

Before these trials took place, the LNER had ordered a further 40 of these A.1 Pacifics, 20 to be built at Doncaster and 20 to be supplied by the North British Locomotive Company of Springburn, Glasgow. The 20 NBL

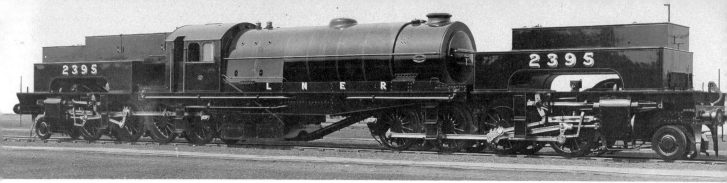

products were all supplied between July and December at a cost of £8,720 each and 15 of these were built to an overall height of 13 ft 3 in (4.04 m) to suit the former NER loading gauge. The first of the Springburn batch was No 2563, named *William Whitelaw* in honour of his position as Chairman of the LNER. The production rate at Doncaster was not quite as rapid and the last of their 20, No 2562, left the 'Plant' in June 1925, by which time the LNER had 52 of the A.1 Pacifics and five of the A.2 type.

Just after the interchange trials, and during the summer of 1925, the LNER staged a magnificent show at Darlington from the 1–3 July in celebrating the Centenary of the opening of the Stockton & Darlington Railway in 1825. This exhibition was opened by the Duke and Duchess of York, then in blissful ignorance of their future role as Monarchs, and the highlight was a procession made up of 54 items of rolling stock. It started

with the Hetton Colliery locomotive of 1822 and finished with a replica of the 1825 train hauled by the original S&DR No 1 *Locomotion*, which incidentally was propelled by a petrol engine hidden in the tender while the fireman fed oily waste into the firebox so as to produce clouds of black smoke.

Among the exhibits were four complete trains of new passenger stock, one from each of the Big Four. The LNER contribution was a train of articulated stock built specially for the Flying Scotsman and hauled by the A.2 Pacific No 2400, *City of Newcastle*. The GWR showed both their Royal Train and a train of articulated stock built to Gresley's patent, the latter being hauled by the former Pacific No 111, *The Great Bear*, which had just been converted to a 4-6-0 and renamed *Viscount Churchill*.

There was one exhibit missing, which was the Reid-MacLeod turbine locomotive which had also been with the Flying Scotsman at the Wembley

The ultimate in Gresleyana. Two sets of 'O'-class wheels with three-cylinder conjugated valve gear, built as a Garrat locomotive in 1925.

Exhibition, but it was a temperamental animal and failed to make the journey from Glasgow to Darlington. The most powerful engine was a 2-8-8-2 Garratt built by Beyer, Peacock & Co of Gorton, Manchester, for the LNER and designed for the banking of 1,000-ton (1016 tonnes) coal trains between Wath and Penistone. The tractive effort of that locomotive, which weighed 174 tons (176.7 tonnes) was 72,940 lb (33,085 kg). So far that figure has not been exceeded in the UK.

As a result of the interchange trials of 1925, the following year saw some alterations in the valve gear of Nos 4477 and 2555. The latter, which had been produced in January 1925, was named *Centenary* in honour of the S&D centenary; on that locomotive the combination lever of the valve gear was lengthened so that the valve travel increased from 4.56 in (11.5 cm) to 5.8 in (14.7 cm) with such spectacular effect that the coal consumption came down from 50 lb (22.7 kg) per mile to 38 lb (17 kg) per mile. As a result of this, all the A.1 Pacifics were modified as they went through the shops for overhaul.

Before this, Gresley had been exploring other ways in which to improve the overall efficiency and so reduce coal consumption. He may have had in mind the achievement of a non-stop run at least to Newcastle-on-Tyne, if not to Edinburgh, and with coal consumption of 50 lb (22.7 kg)

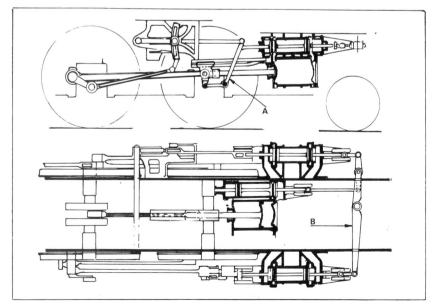

Gresley three-cylinder conjugated valve gear.
A. Combination lever
B. 2:1 conjugating lever

ALCO 'Hudson' locomotive of 1927.

per mile, the latter was not possible with a tender holding only eight tons (8.1 tonnes) of coal. One possible method of improving efficiency was by the use of much higher boiler pressures and since 1924 discussions had been going on with the boiler firm of Yarrow, with the idea of using a marine type of water tube boiler at around 500 lb per sq in pressure. By 1927 the boiler design had been evolved and an order placed for its construction, together with that for a special locomotive chassis on which it could be accommodated, and this was to have its effect on the later designs of Gresley's Pacific locomotives.

In July 1927 No 4480 *Enterprise* was fitted with a new boiler working at 220 lb per sq in, which increased its tractive effort to 36,465 lb (16,540 kg); the thicker boiler plates also increased its weight to 152.6 tons (155 tonnes) with an axle load on the driving wheels of 22.05 tons (22.4 tonnes). Apparently the Civil Engineer had no objection to that figure, since the three-cylinder arrangement was so easy on the track. In that year four others, Nos 2544, 2573, 2578 and 2580, were also fitted with the higher pressure boilers and, of these, No 2544 *Lemberg* had its cylinder bore reduced from 20 in (51 cm) to 18.25 in (46 cm). This restored its tractive effort to the original amount, so that comparative tests could be run with one of the others still working at the original pressure of 180 lb per sq in.

A.1 Pacific No. 4478 on relief 'Flying Scotsman' leaving Kings Cross.

Also during 1927, the other three Groups all came out with new 4-6-0 locomotives; the LMS with their 'Royal Scots'; the Southern with their 'Lord Nelson' class and the Great Western with the 'King' class. The latter was again claimed to be the most powerful engine in the UK, with a tractive effort of 40,300 lb (18,280 kg). By way of comparison, in October 1927 ALCO produced a 'Hudson' class 4-6-4 for the New York Central with 79 in (2 m) driving wheels and a tractive effort of 53,200 lb (24,131 kg) including a booster. They were called the 'Hudson' class, because the New York Central followed the Hudson River on its way north out of New York to Albany. The extra wheel at the back was to accommodate a larger firebox with a firegrate area of 81.5 sq ft (24.8 sq m), so as to give ample steaming capacity.

During the summer of 1927, the relief Flying Scotsman ran non-stop daily down from Kings Cross to Newcastle, a distance of 268.3 miles (432 km), thus capturing the record for a daily run held by the Great Western since 1906 for the 225.7 miles (363 km) to Plymouth. Gresley still had to beat *Ionic*'s 1895 run of 299 miles (481 km) to Carlisle, which was no doubt still in his memory.

In February 1928 some trials took place between No 4473 *Solario*, with a boiler pressure of 180 lb per sq in, and No 2544 *Lemberg*, with a 220 lb per sq in boiler. These results were not very conclusive since the performance of both was about equal, but a decision was taken to convert all the A.1s to 220-lb boilers and to reduce the cylinder bore to 19 in (48 cm).

1 May 1928 was the Red Letter Day of that year for the LNER. It saw the inauguration of the non-stop run of 392.7 miles (632 km) from Kings Cross to Edinburgh (Waverley) in both directions during the summer months for the Flying Scotsman. To accomplish this, five special corridor tenders had been built, in conditions of great secrecy, so that the crews could be ex-

Route diagram of the 'Flying Scotsman' from Kings Cross to Edinburgh, showing gradients, tunnels and water troughs.

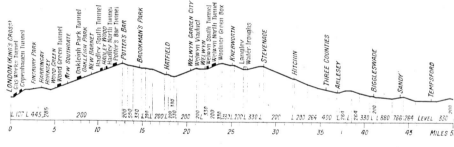

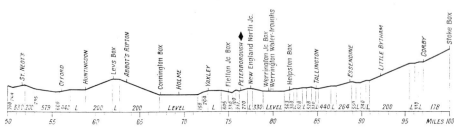

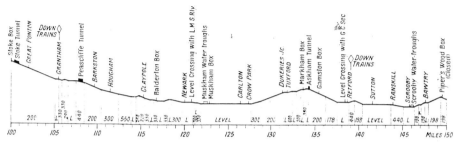

changed half way. Those tenders were fitted to locomotives Nos 4472 *Flying Scotsman*; 4476 *Royal Lancer*; 2573 *Harvester*; 2577 *Night Hawk* and 2580 *Shotover*.

The two chosen for the initial runs were No 4472 for the down journey and No 2580 for the up run. Each train consisted of 11 coaches, weighing in all 350 tons (355.6 tonnes), which included a triplet dining car set and one coach with a hair-dressing saloon. The drivers on No 4472 were A. Pibworth and Tom Blades, who had been the fireman on the North Eastern 4-4-0 No 1620 in the 1895 'Race to the North'.

The departure from Kings Cross was witnessed by an enormous number of spectators and the official send-off was by the Lord Mayor of London, Sir Charles Batho, and of course by Nigel Gresley himself. The up train was greeted on arrival by the LNER Chairman, William Whitelaw.

The times of the down run are shown in the table below:

The up train was passed at 2.02 pm, just 204 miles (328 km) from London, and arrived at Kings Cross at 6.12 pm. The coal consumption in each case was around seven tons (7.1 tonnes), equivalent to 40 lb (18 kg) per mile, so the eight-ton (8.12-tonnes) tender was adequate. In fact, with careful stacking, at least another ton of coal could be added, which was sufficient for the summer season when there was little heating load and weather conditions were not too adverse. These loads and speeds were a comparatively easy job for these A.1 Pacifics, whether with the 180 lb or the 220-lb boiler. By way of a show of defiance, the LMS had staged a couple of non-stop runs on 27 April from Euston to both Edinburgh and Glasgow. For that event it had divided its Royal Scot train into two portions, of which the Glasgow part consisted of nine coaches and was worked over the 401.4 miles (646 km) by Royal Scot locomotive No 6113 *Cameronian*. The Edinburgh section of five coaches was hauled by a Midland Compound 4-4-0 No 1054. The latter was a most creditable effort since the normal capacity of its tender was only 5.5 tons (5.58 tonnes) of coal and so for the 399.7 miles (643 km) this implied a coal consumption of under 31 lb (14 kg) per mile; even if an extra ton was added by careful stacking, it was still a skilful piece of firing and driving.

These non-stop runs of the Flying Scotsman were the first occasion on which a train had been worked through Newcastle without stopping. A study of the layout of the rail system through Newcastle shows why very little time is gained by omitting the Newcastle stop, since the speed over several miles of that area was limited to 30 mph (48 km/h); however, although the time saving may have been only

	Distance (miles/km)		Average overall speed (mph/km/h)
Kings Cross (depart)		10.00 am	
Peterborough	76.4/122.9	11.24	54.6/87.8
Grantham	105.5/169.7	11.58	53.6/86.2
Doncaster	156 /251	12.54	53.8/86.5
York	188.2/302.8	1.38 pm	51.8/83.3
Newcastle	268.3/431.7	3.22	50.0/80.5
Berwick	335.2/539.4	4.50	49.0/78.8
Edinburgh	392.7/631.9	6.03	48.8/78.5

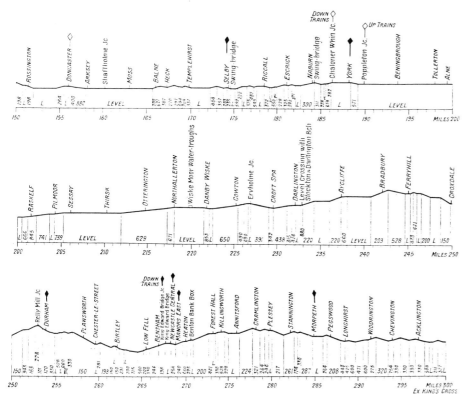

a few minutes, the prestige of a non-stop run of almost 400 miles (644 km) was enormous.

A further problem in relation to long non-stop runs was water consumption. A steam locomotive necessarily consumed water at a rate that would make any beer-drinking Rugby player jealous. As a rough guide, the boiler would produce 10 lb (4.5 kg) of steam for every pound of coal burnt, which implies a consumption of 500 lb (227 kg) or 50 gallons (227 litres) per mile. The total amount of water used by all the railways in Great Britain at that time was 16,130 million gallons (73,327 million litres) a year, costing £503,000, which was quite an expense and a handling problem.

The feature that enabled long non-stop runs to be achieved was the water pick-up apparatus, devised by Ramsbottom at Crewe in 1860 and first used near Llandudno Junction for the Irish Mail. The non-stop run of the Flying Scotsman was

possible only by reason of six sets of water troughs laid on the main line at Langley (Stevenage), at Werrington (just north of Peterborough), at Muskham (near Newark), at Scrooby (between Retford and Doncaster), at Wiske Moor (Northallerton) and at Lucker (13 miles beyond Alnmouth). The longest distance between any of these sets of troughs was the 96 miles (154.5 km) from Wiske Moor to Lucker. That was because the halfway spot between these two would have been at Newcastle-upon-Tyne and it was never envisaged that trains would not stop at that station. With a 5,000-gallon (22,730-litre) tender, and using water at 50 gallons (227 litres) a mile, that stretch could prove critical if the filling at the previous troughs had not been fully effective.

The pick-up scoop had to be lowered by a hand-operated mechanism, but it was almost impossible to pull the scoop up

out of the water at any speed. In order to avoid overfilling, which would mean water pouring all over the following coaches, the scoop was lowered in at a point along the trough commensurate with the amount of water needed. These troughs were 400–600 yards (366–549 m) long and rested on the sleepers between the running rails; of course they had to be laid on a completely level piece of track and be located near a suitable supply of water that was not too hard in quality and not too expensive. In the days when these troughs were installed, there was almost no problem in using local rivers or canals, where these were handy, and in some cases the railways bored their own wells.

The pick-up scoop was some 10 in (25 cm) wide and dipped into the water about two inches (6 cm); the quantity of water picked up could be up to 3,500 gallons (15,911 litres) and the rate of pick-up at 60 mph (96.5 km/h) would be almost $\frac{3}{4}$ ton (0.762 tonnes) per second. The retardation load on the tender during the pick-up would have been in the region of 500 lb (227 kg). These water troughs were not used much outside the UK because most railways did not fence in their track and they would have been used as a local water hole, but they were used in the USA by both the New York Central and the Pennsylvania Railroads on their competitive routes between New York and Chicago. Their tenders had special vents along each side to take the overflow, but on British tenders the overflow was by means of the usual filling orifice at the back of the tender; the flap on that was allowed to be loosely attached, but on more than one occasion it opened by mistake, producing a column of water several feet high which fell back onto the following coaches with a considerable impact.

Class A3: The Super Pacifics, 1928-1935

The first two A.3 class Pacifics were produced from 'The Plant' in August 1928. They had 220 lb-per sq in boiler pressure and three 19-in (48-cm) diameter cylinders with a tractive effort of 32,909 lb (14,928 kg). Their weight was 96.25 tons (97.79 tonnes) for the engine and 57.9 tons (58.8 tonnes) for the tender, which was of a new non-corridor type holding the usual eight tons (8.12 tonnes) of coal and 5,000 gallons (22,730 litres) of water. The overall height was reduced to 13 ft 1 in (4 m) so as to provide wider route availability. The first two, numbered 2743 *Felstead* and 2744 *Grand Parade*, were followed at the rate of one per month until No 2752 *Spion Kop*, which came out in April 1927. The name *Spion Kop* seems rather an odd one to choose either for a horse or for a locomotive, since it was our most disastrous battle in the whole of the Boer War.

These A.3s were built with the 5.8-in (15-cm) valve travel and with an improved big end floating bush. Also, the piston rings were narrower at 0.31 in (0.79 cm), against those of 0.75 in (1.9 cm)

used previously, and proved freer in running. The driving position was on the left hand side for the first time, so as to provide better visibility for signals. The colour light type were being installed on some portions of the main line and were sited for visibility from the left side of the cab. Some of these A.3s were allocated to the difficult Waverley route between Edinburgh and Carlisle, with its 10-mile (16-km) grades of 1 in 70/75, where they could handle unassisted the 400-ton (406-tonnes) trains such as the *Thames-Forth* from St Pancras to Edinburgh.

At the end of 1929 the high-pressure compound locomotive No 10000 was produced from the Darlington Works with its Yarrow water tube boiler that had been ordered in 1927. This was on a 4-6-4 wheel arrangement— not strictly a Pacific—but was the first of Gresley's locomotives to bear a streamlined design that was to affect the future Pacific layout. In the layout of No 10000 the streamlined front was imposed because of the shape of the boiler, which allowed no room for a conventional chimney,

and the front end had to be designed to take the smoke clear of the driver's cab. The boiler was designed to work at 450 lb per sq in and there were two high-pressure cylinders, 12 in (30 cm) in diameter by 26 in (66 cm) stroke, and two low-pressure cylinders, 20 in by 26 in (51x66 cm). The total weight of the engine and tender was 166 tons (168.6 tonnes).

Unfortunately, far from proving more efficient, as was hoped, this engine was a disaster from the start and could barely maintain a steam pressure of 300 lb per sq in on its first outing. It did once haul the Flying Scotsman from Edinburgh to London, but its coal consumption was greater than any of the Pacifics owing to leaks in its boiler casing and it would not steam at all well. It was rudely called 'The Galloping Sausage' by footplate crews and after various trials and modifications it was fitted with an A.4 type boiler in 1937 and finished life as BR No 60700.

In 1930 a further eight A.3s were produced between February and June with numbers 2595/9 and 2795/7, all being named after racehorses; trials were carried out on No 2576 (180-lb boiler) and No 2580 (220-lb boiler) when fitted with ACFI water heaters but without any

High-pressure compound locomotive No. 10000 of 1929.

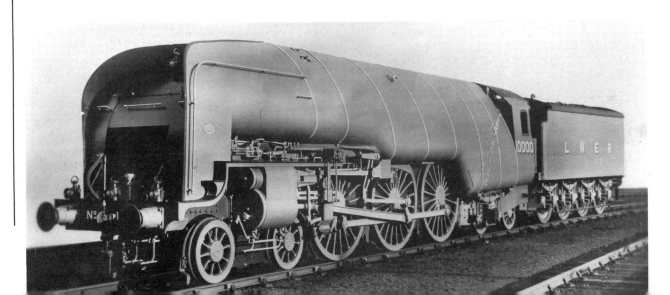

improvement in performance or in fuel consumption.

By 1932 it was becoming evident that the conjugated valve gear was subject to wear on all the pin joints in the system, one serious result of which was to cause considerable variations in the cylinder output, due to the different port opening times in the three piston valves. Some indicator trials were carried out on No 2751 *Humorist*, which showed differences in cylinder performance as listed below.

The location of the conjugated valve gear at the front of the cylinders was partly to blame, in that the lubrication was dried off by wind and was prone to be affected by ash and cinders from the smoke box. In the case of some other three-cylinder loco-motives, where the conjugated gear was arranged behind the cylinders, that gear was better lubricated by the steam and oil from the cylinders and did not suffer from the same wear problems as on these Pacifics. The load discrepancy became greater with increased speed and this was to be a clue to some of the later problems with these engines in service, and particu-larly on high speed runs.

With 70 of these Pacifics now in service, there were sufficient to provide stand-by locomotives for the non-stop Flying Scots-man. These were organised with Pacifics available at Grantham, Doncaster and Newcastle, while some Ivatt 'Atlantics' were held available at Hitchin, Peter-borough, York, Darlington and Tweedmouth. Those locomotives were available for other duties once the Flying Scotsman had

safely gone by and were only used as replacements about five times in each summer season.

In 1933 there occurred in Germany one of the most signifi-cant events in the railway story—the inauguration of a high speed diesel train called 'Die Fliegende Hamburger'. It was only a two-coach unit, but was fitted with two of the new Maybach high-speed diesel engines, Type GO, each producing 410 hp at 1,400 rpm. The train ran between Berlin and Hamburg at an average speed of 77.4 mph (124.5 km/h), with a maximum speed of 103 mph (166 km/h), and displaced the GWR Chelten-ham Express, which at that time averaged 66.4 mph (107 km/h) from Swindon to Paddington, as the fastest train in the world.

On the LNER, train speeds had not increased much since the Pacifics were first introduced ten years earlier, but, with the increased demand for passenger comfort, train weights had gone on increasing. They were often around the 500-ton (508-tonnes) mark, and sometimes as much as 630 tons (640 tonnes). As well as demands for greater comfort, there were those for greater speed, one of the con-tributary factors being the abolition of the speed limit on roads which took place as a result of the 1930 Road Traffic Act. The previous speed limit of 20 mph (32 km/h) had been largely ignored, but this abolition made it possible for bus oper-ators and private motorists to plan road journeys for average speeds of around 30 mph (48 km/h).

The LNER asked the German railcar makers to produce a

Cab of locomotive No. 10000.

schedule for a Flying Newcastler based on a three-car unit carrying 140 passengers and fitted with the turbocharged Maybach engine, then rated at 620 hp. At the same time a trial run was undertaken from Kings Cross to Leeds on 30 November 1934 with the A.1 Pacific No 4472 and a light train of 147 tons (149.3 tonnes) which included the dynamometer car. On that occasion the down run of 186.8 miles (300.6 km) was covered in 152 minutes (73.7 mph/118.6 km/h) with a minimum speed up Stoke bank of 82 mph (132 km/h); the output was estimated at 1,145 drawbar hp. On the return run, the load was increased to six cars (207 tons/210 tonnes) and the overall time was 157 minutes. A maximum speed of 100 mph (161 km/h) was recorded momentarily down Stoke Bank on the descent from Corby and 24 miles (39 km) were run at an average of 90.2 mph (145 km/h). The speeds at the various water troughs were kept down to around 80 mph (129 km/h), so presumably there was no difficulty in picking up water at those speeds. The coal

Indicated Horse Power

Speed	Cut off	L.H. cylinder	Centro cylinder	R H cylinder	Total
43 (69)	30%	463	513	527	1503
57 (92)	25%	460	553	518	1531
63 (101)	20%	384	547	472	1403
75 (121)	20%	402	585	480	1437

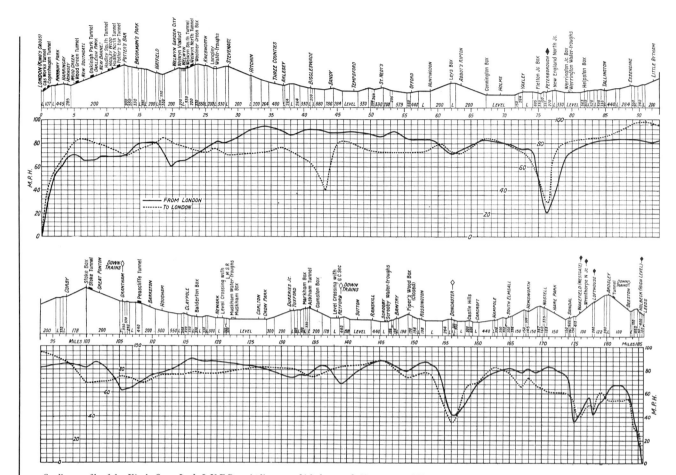

Gradient profile of the King's Cross–Leeds L.N.E.R. main line over which the remarkable test runs of November 30 were made at the speeds shown by the two graphs

Severe speed restrictions shown by black diamonds, slight restrictions by white diamonds

consumption was high, at 54 lb (24.5 kg) per mile for such a light train, but No 4472 was still fitted with its original 180-lb boiler and had run by then 653,000 miles (296,200 km).

The best schedule that could be produced by the diesel railcar for the 268 miles to Newcastle was 257 minutes (62.5 mph/ 100.6 km/h). As a result of the run on 30 November, it was calculated that this could be

improved by the use of an A.3 type and a trial run was organised on 5 March 1935. On that occasion No 2750 *Papyrus* was set to haul a six-car train, including the dynamometer car and a first class diner, weighing in all 217 tons (220.4 tonnes). The total train weight including the locomotive came to 375.5 tons (381.5 tonnes). The down run was accomplished in 237 minutes and the up run in 232

Log of first LNER High-Speed Run of 30 November 1934.

minutes. The times were as shown in the table below:

The speed limits then in force were 70 mph (112 km/h) at Offord, 20 mph (32 km/h) at Peterborough, 65 mph (104.6 km/h) at Grantham, 40 mph (64.3 km/h) at Selby, 25 mph (40.2 km/h) at York, 30 mph (48.2 km/h) at Durham and 25

		DOWN			UP	
	Miles	Times	Average speed (mph/km/h)	Miles	Times	Average speed (mph/km/h)
Kings Cross				268.3	232	69.4 (111.6)
Peterborough	76.4	63	72.8 (117.16)	191.9	170	67.7 (109)
Grantham	105.5			162.8	149	65.6 (105.5)
Doncaster	156	132	70.9 (114)	112.3	106	63.6 (102.3)
York	188.2	165	68.4 (110)	80.1	72	66.8 (107.5)
Darlington	232.3			36	39	55.4 (89.1)
Newcastle	268.3	237	67.9 (109.2)	—	—	—

mph (40.2 km/h) on the King Edward Bridge at the approach to Newcastle.

These two runs produced a number of speed records, including a maximum speed of 108 mph (173.8 km/h) at Tallington on the descent from Stoke Box summit and the following:

536.6 miles at 70.4 mph
   (863.5 km at 113.2 km/h)
500.2 miles at 73 mph
   (804.9 km at 117.4 km/h)
300 miles at 80.1 mph
   (482.7 km at 128.9 km/h)
12.3 miles at 100.6 mph
   (19.8 km at 161.8 km/h)

These were records for steam traction only, since it must be remembered that a speed of 135 mph (217 km/h) had been achieved by an electric railcar in 1903 and 143 mph (230 km/h) by the Krukenburg propellor car in 1932, both in Germany. The coal consumption for these two runs was much better and amounted to 44.9 lb (20.3 kg) per mile, including that used for lighting up, or not much over 40 lb (18 kg) per mile on the actual runs.

While these speed trials had been going on, the last batch of A.3 Pacifics had been produced from Doncaster. There were nine of these, from No 2500 *Windsor Lad* to No 2508 *Brown Jack*, which came out in January 1953 and was the last of the A.3 type, generally known as 'Super Pacifics'. These last nine were fitted with an improved type of steam collector, with a series of troughs through which the steam had to pass to the regulator. This was designed to prevent 'priming', or the passing of water-saturated steam, which could cause damage if it ever got to the cylinders. These steam collectors were covered with a banjo-shaped steel pressing which was

Weight diagram of streamlined 'Mikado' locomotives, Class P.2, later to be rebuilt as Pacifics.

later fitted on other A.3-type engines, as well as those of the A.1 category when they were equipped with the 220-lb (99.7-kg) boilers.

These last nine engines all carried the names of racehorses, as had 37 of the A.1s and 24 of the A.3 class. Doncaster has long been an important place in the horse racing business and, whenever there was a race meeting there, special trains used to come from all parts of the country. The choice of these names was both a tribute to this useful source of revenue as well as proclaiming these locomotives as fleet of foot, though that characteristic was only just beginning to emerge.

Before leaving the conventional Pacifics, of which 79 had been built between 1922 and 1935, we must go back to 1929. M. André Chapelon, then an unknown Development Engineer on the Paris-Orleans Railway, rebuilt one of their Pacific locomotives, No 3566, in a scientific manner and increased its output by 50 per cent. That particular engine had been so sluggish it had been called 'Le cholera', but after its rebuild it was transformed and could produce over 3,000 IHP. This was achieved by a redesign of the steam pipes, a new regulator, a larger superheater, a steel firebox with a Nicholson thermic syphon and, above all, by the use of the twin Kylchap exhaust system; the last feature was a Chapelon improvement on the Kylala exhaust splitter, designed

by a Finnish engineer of that name. These points were carefully studied by Gresley and a number of them adopted in his design of a 2-8-2 (1-D-1) Mikado type locomotive, produced in May 1934, intended to work the heavy passenger trains between Edinburgh and Aberdeen. That route, 130.5 miles (210 km) long, included a number of short steep grades, mostly at 1-in-100, and the train loads were sometimes beyond the capacity of an unaided Pacific. The first of this new Mikado type, class P.2, was No 2001 *Cock o' the North* which was sent over to the French locomotive testing station at Vitry-sur-Seine before going into service. Prior to that it had made a demonstration run with a 649-ton (659-tonnes) train and had reached 76 mph (122 km/h) on level track. No 2001 was equipped with poppet valves, but its sister engine, No 2002 *Earl Marischal*, was fitted with the usual Gresley valve gear. The front end of these two was similar to that used in the high pressure compound No 10000 and was evolved as a result of experiments at the City & Guilds College of Engineering with the intention of keeping the exhaust steam clear of the driver's view; however, on No 2002 the exhaust was so gentle that extra deflector plates had to be added. There were to be four more of this P.2 class and their design was to have an influence on the layout of the next design of Pacifics known as the A.4 class.

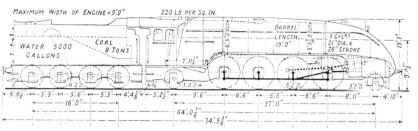

GRESLEY MIKADO OF 1934 WITH A3 BOILER AND VALVE GEAR

The A4 Streamliners 1935-1939

This period has been described as four glorious years for the LNER and indeed it was, in so far as locomotive performance was concerned. But financially it was far from true, for net income had fallen steadily from £14 million in 1923 to £9 million in 1935. Although there was a small improvement in 1937 to £10 million, this was down again to £6 million by 1938, due to troubles in the steel industry. The worst year had been 1926, when the General Strike had reduced profits to only £4.6 million—but they were still profits, unlike the situation since Nationalisation in 1948. All this had its effect on the provision of new locomotives and on the equipment in the works, which in turn affected the quality of the locomotives produced.

Following the high-speed run on 5 March 1935, the General Manager, Ralph Wedgwood, proposed that a four-hour schedule be adopted for a special train between London and Newcastle, with one stop at Darlington.

This was to coincide with the Silver Jubilee of King George V, whose name the train would carry. To provide the motive power, Gresley designed an improved version of the A.3 class, with a higher boiler pressure at 250 lb per sq in and with three cylinders of 18.5 in (46.9 cm) diameter. With a stroke of 26 in (66 cm) and with 80-in (203-cm) driving wheels, this produced a tractive effort of 35,455 lb (16,082 kg). The influence of M. Chapelon was evident in the layout of the steam pipes, but the Kylchap exhaust was not at first fitted; instead there was a new type of blast pipe with a jumper top. The most significant improvement was in the adoption of a streamlined front end, which was intended to reduce wind resistance and keep the exhaust steam well clear of the cab.

Tests carried out at the National Physical Laboratory with wooden models, based on the shape of some railcars designed by M. Ettore Bugatti (of racing car fame), showed that power savings of up to 190 hp at 100 mph (160 km/h) might be obtained. These figures were afterwards disputed and, in any event, the effect of a side wind on the much larger area of a whole train had considerably more effect on power requirements than that of the relatively small frontal area. The shape of the front nose was, however, much more beneficial in preventing the steam from blocking the driver's view, which was a crucial matter given the small cab window space available and the importance of not missing signals at the greater operating speeds.

Other improvements on the A.3 design were the use of 9-in (22.8-cm) diameter piston valves, a reduction in the length of the boiler tubes by 12 in (30.5 cm), an increase in the loading of the bogie control springs to a maximum of seven tons (7.1 tonnes) and the adoption of wedge-shaped cab fronts which helped to improve the driver's visibility. Just before this, some experiments in air deflection had been carried out by M. Pottier on the cabs of locomotives on the Nord Railway in France, where a steel sheet protruding a few inches from the cab side gave the driver considerable protection when looking out. Previously nearly all drivers in France were to be seen wearing motorcycle-type goggles on the footplate. This deflection device was adopted on the new A.4 Pacifics as a glass screen about 3 in (7.6 cm) wide between the two cab windows, giving the driver much better visibility without getting grit and dust in his eyes.

The adhesive weight of the new A.4 Pacific was 66 tons (67 tonnes), with a total engine weight of 109.9 tons (111.6 tonnes). The streamlined tender

First Trial Run of 'Silver Jubilee' Express with locomotive No. 2509, *Silver Link*.

carried nine tons (9.1 tonnes) of coal and 5,000 gallons of water, weighing 60.3 tons (61.2 tonnes) when full. Under the outer streamlined skin, the boiler and firebox were insulated with five layers of Alfol foil. The locomotive was finished in silver and grey, as was the whole train which consisted of seven coaches, made up of a twin articulated brake-third, a triplet restaurant car set and another twin articulated first and third class pair. The train weight was 220 tons (223 tonnes) and provided 198 seats, for which supplementary fares of 3/- (15p) for third and 5/- (25p) for first class were charged. It was claimed that in three years these supplementary fees paid for the cost of the train. The coach bodies had fairings below the underframe between the bogies to reduce air resistance and the coach ends were joined up by air smooth rubber sheeting outside the normal corridor connections.

From the high-speed run of 5 March, the whole train was finished and ready for service by September with two locomotives, No 2509 *Silver Link* and No 2510 *Quicksilver*. A trial run to Cambridge was followed on 27 September by a demonstration run for the Press, which electrified not only the reporters but also some of the LNER officials themselves. After passing through Hatfield (17.7 miles or 28.5 km) in 17 minutes, a speed of 107 mph (172 km/h) was attained through Hitchin and was followed by a maximum of 112.5 mph (181 km/h) at Arlesey; for 43 miles (69 km) the average was 100 mph (161 km/h). Peterborough was passed in 55 minutes at an average of 83 mph (133 km/h) and Grantham (105.5 miles or 169 km) was reached in 88 minutes. The locomotive rode beautifully, but the same could not be said of the coaches. However the

problem was overcome by the fitting of some rubber blocks between the bogie bolsters and the side stops, after which the ride was considerably improved.

Since only two of the locomotives were available when the full public service started on 30 September 1935, one was kept in reserve and No 2509 *Silver Link* worked the train both ways each weekday for three weeks, running 2,700 miles (4345 km) each week in this high-speed service. As with the start of the non-stop Flying Scotsman runs in 1928, there were huge crowds to see the train arrive

Newcastle	Depart	10.00 am	Arrive	9.30 pm
Darlington	Arrive	10.40 am	Depart	8.50 pm
	Depart	10.42 am	Arrive	8.48 pm
Kings Cross	Arrive	2.00 pm	Depart	5.30 pm

The portion between Darlington and Kings Cross was run at an average speed of 70.4 mph (113.2 km/h).

On 27 August 1936 there occurred one of the most amazing of the high-speed runs by an A.4 class engine when a dynamometer car was added to the train with the intention of carrying out some operational

and depart from Kings Cross. It may have carried Gresley's mind back to that day at Crewe in 1895 when the West Coast took the honours in speed, but the East Coast was now revenged by his efforts.

The next two of the A.4 class came out in November and December, Nos 2511 and 2512 named *Silver King* and *Silver Fox*. The LNER produced a very handsome table paperweight model of *Silver Link* and it would be interesting to know how many of these are still in existence. The timing of the Silver Jubilee run was:

analysis. Usually when tests were carried out on a new class of engine, a shelter was erected at the front of the smokebox and observers in the shelter took measurements of steam pressures, exhaust pressure and temperature, together with an analysis of the smokebox gasses. On these wedge-nosed A.4 Pacifics it was not possible to

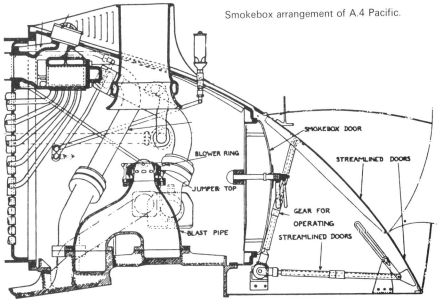

Smokebox arrangement of A.4 Pacific.

erect such a shelter, so much of the information had to be obtained by remote reading of instruments in the dynamometer car. On that occasion the locomotive No 2512 *Silver Fox* was maintaining a steady speed of around 70 mph (112.6 km/h) up the 1-in-200 from Grantham to Stoke Box summit, but steam pressure was falling and the speed came down to 67 mph (108 km/h) at the summit. Normally this train ran down the section from Stoke Box to Werrington at around 95 mph (153 km/h), since that speed could comfortably be achieved at a cut-off of around 15–20 per cent without working the engine too hard and gave the fireman a chance to build up the fire after the climb from Grantham. Some five miles (8 km) down the grade from the summit, the speed had built up to 90 mph (145 km/h). Edward Thompson, then Mechanical Engineer for the Southern Area of the LNER, came through the corridor tender from the dynamometer

car and told the driver to 'top the hundred mark'.

In order to work up to 100 mph (160.9 km/h), the power output had to be increased and so the cut-off was put up to 35 per cent; speed then rose to the 100 mph figure some two miles (3.2 km) further on. Not content with that, the speed went on increasing until 113 mph (182 km/h) was attained at the 87-mile (140-km) post between Essendine and Tallington. After that it had to be reduced fairly rapidly to 80 mph (129 km/h) for the troughs at Werrington and then to 20 mph (32 km/h) for the Peterborough speed limit.

The driver may have suspected that all was not right with the locomotive and been reluctant to do a high speed run down Stoke Bank, but he obeyed the instruction. Seventy miles (112 km) further on, at Hatfield, the centre big end bearing overheated and broke up, resulting in the piston knocking both ends out of the centre cylinder. The run was then completed at reduced speed and

arrived at Kings Cross seven minutes late; they were lucky to finish safely since the connecting rod might have fractured, which could have derailed the locomotive with possibly disastrous results.

It would seem that Edward Thompson had not been on any of the previous high-speed runs and wanted to see how these A.4 locomotives performed. He was probably told off by Gresley over this event and it was known that he did not like the Gresley design of conjugated valve motion. This may have contributed to the events that took place after 1941 during his term as C.M.E. of the LNER.

On the return run of the Silver Jubilee that same day, the failed *Silver Fox* was replaced by No 2509 *Silver Link* and the top speed was limited to 90 mph (145 km/h). The outstanding feature of that run was the climb to Stoke Box, when the

No. 4498 *Sir Nigel Gresley* with its designer alongside.

No. 4468 *Mallard*, the first A.4 to be fitted with the Kylchap Exhaust System, now preserved at York.

speed did not fall below 75 mph (121 km/h), and the whole journey was completed four minutes ahead of schedule.

Operationally, this one high-speed train was a bit of a liability because of the problem of braking from high speed with the British system of vacuum brakes then in common use. That meant that an extra block section, in which no train could be allowed, had to be maintained ahead of the Silver Jubilee. That, however, could not be applied to the new electric colour-light-controlled section between York and Northallerton which had been installed in 1933, so the speed over this, potentially one of the fastest pieces of track, was limited nominally to 80 mph (129 km/h).

During 1936, some significant events in the railway world were taking place. Among these should be mentioned the fastest steam train in regular service in the world, the 'Detroit Arrow' of the Pennsylvania Railroad, which ran the 141 miles (227 km) from Fort Wayne to Englewood in 115 minutes (73.6 mph or 118.5 km/h). In Germany on 11 May, a Borsig 4-6-4 steam locomotive No 05.002 had been timed at 124.3 mph (200 km/h), and one of their three-car diesel trains had achieved 127 mph (204.4 km/h). The outstanding achieve-

ment of 1936 occurred on 23 October when the Denver-Zephyr diesel train operated by the Chicago, Burlington & Quincey R.R. ran the 1,017 miles (1,637 km) from Chicago to Denver *non-stop* at a speed of 83.3 mph (134 km/h) in 732 minutes. That train, which weighed 465 tons (472 tonnes), ran for 445 miles (716 km) at 91.6 mph (147.5 km/h), reached a maximum of 116 mph (187 km/h) and consumed 1.28 gallons (5.8 litres) of fuel per mile. The train was powered by two diesel-electric units built by the Electro-Motive Division of General Motors, which was eventually to cause the cessation of steam locomotive building almost throughout the world.

On 16/17 November, the LNER's rival West Coast LMS Railway ran a pair of high-speed trains between Euston and Glasgow, when the journey of 401.4 miles (646 km) was run non-stop in the down direction in 353.6 minutes and in the up direction in 344.2 minutes. The locomotive in each case was their Pacific No 6201 *Princess Elizabeth* and the train weights were 230 tons (234 tonnes) for the down run and 260 tons (264 tonnes) for the up journey. That was over a much more arduous route than on the East Coast and included the ascents to 400 ft (122 m) at Tring and at Kilsby, as well as to 916 ft (280 m) at Shap and 1,014 ft (309 m) at Beattock.

During all this, the LNER had not been idle and had carried out some test runs with No 2511 *Silver King* between Newcastle and Edinburgh. With a train weight of 252 tons (256 tonnes), the 124.4 miles (200.2 km) had been run in 114 minutes (only one minute more than that of the 1895 Race time). Also, Herbert Nigel Gresley had received his knighthood and on 23 October had given his Address as President of the Institution of Mechanical Engineers. Finally, to round off the year, Doncaster produced two of the last series of thirty A.4 Pacifics, starting with No 4482 *Golden Eagle* and finishing with No 4903 *Peregrine* in June 1938; all but eight of these were to carry the names of birds.

Nos 4482 to 4487 were finished in LNER green, but the next five, which all carried Imperial names, were finished in blue with black frontal noses and were intended for use on a new streamlined express called *Coronation*. This was in honour of the coronation of King George VI, who as The Duke of York had opened the 1925 Centenary Exhibition at Darlington and with whom Gresley had paid a visit to the Romney, Hythe & Dymchurch Railway in 1926. That railway had commissioned the Colchester firm of Davey Paxman to build some replicas of the A.1 Pacifics for their 15-in (38.1-cm) gauge line and The Duke of York and Gresley had gone to have a ride on one of them. These replicas, designed by Henry Greenley, were two-cylinder models, and the builders were the same firm who were later to build the Valenta diesel engines for the High Speed Trains, also to run on the former LNER track.

The 'Coronation' consisted of a nine-coach train, weighing 325 tons (330 tonnes), and the last coach was a special beaver-tailed observation car which only ran in the summer season. The whole train was finished in light Marlborough blue above the waistline and dark garter blue below, and was made up of four pairs of articulated coaches seating 216 passengers. The service was inaugurated on 5 July 1937. A special demonstration run was carried out on 30 June, hauled by No 4489 *Dominion of Canada*, when a top speed of 109 mph (175 km/h) was achieved. It was perhaps as well that nothing more spectacular was attempted as on the previous day the Press had gone on the first run of the rival LMS 'Coronation Scot'; a speed of 114 mph (183.5 km/h), reached just two miles short of Crewe, nearly resulted in a derailment at the entrance to Crewe station. Some of the guests opted out of the return trip.

In September 1937 a third streamlined train, known as the 'West Riding Limited', was put into service from Bradford and Leeds to London. That was an eight-coach train similar to *Coronation*, but without the observation car, and was scheduled for an overall speed of 68 mph (109.5 km/h). Two special engines were provided for that service, Nos 4495–6 named *Golden Fleece* and *Golden Shuttle*, painted in blue and black, as were all the A.4 class from October 1937.

In November, three A.4 class came out from Doncaster and one of these, the 100th Pacific built, No 4498, was named *Sir Nigel Gresley* at a ceremonial unveiling at Marylebone station by the LNER Chairman, William Whitelaw, on 26 November.

1937 ended on a note of tragedy for the A.3 Pacific No 2744 *Grand Parade* when that was involved in an accident at Castlecary, on the old North British line between Edinburgh and Glasgow. On 10 December, on a snowy evening, *Grand Parade* with a nine-coach train ran into the rear of a Dundee train which had been halted at some points blocked by snow. The impact took place at nearly 60 mph (96.5 km/h) and the momentum of the train was calculated as 54,000 ft-tons. Though 35 passengers were killed and 179 injured, the footplate crew was safe and some of the passengers in the rear coaches got out at the station unaware that a major disaster had taken place. The accident was blamed partially on poor visibility due to steam on the cab. Some wind deflectors were then tried out on No 2751 *Humorist*, but without any real beneficial results.

The ultimate development in the A.4 class came when No 4468 *Mallard* was produced in February 1938 with a Kylchap twin blastpipe, following some trials with a set of these also on No 2571 *Humorist*. The final three, Nos 4901/2/3, also had this Kylchap fitment and their performance was much improved. It seems odd that this device had not been tried much earlier on the A.4 class since it had been used on the P.2 Mikado engines for the Scottish services built in 1934.

The problem of brakes for the higher speeds in service was of concern not only to the LNER. The Westinghouse Brake Company designed a system, termed QSA (Quick Service Application), which they persuaded the LNER to test in service. This was fitted first on some suburban stock and a set was then fitted to the coaches of one of the 'Coronation' trains, which resulted in a test being arranged to try the system at high speed.

The result was the high-speed run of No 4468 *Mallard* on 3 July 1938. It ran with the dynamometer car and six coaches of the reserve set, weighing in all 240 tons (244 tonnes), from Wood Green to Grantham and turned the complete train on the triangle at Barkston. Setting out south from Grantham, a speed of 74.5 mph (120 km/h) had been reached by the summit at Stoke Box and, with full regulator and 40 per cent cut-off, the speed reached

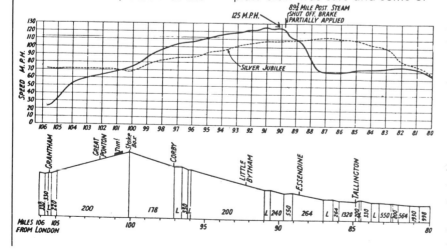

The log of *Mallard*'s run of 3 July 1938, from Grantham to Mile Post 80.

Last visit to Kings Cross of Raven Pacific No. 2401 before withdrawal in 1937.

116 mph (187 km/h) down the grade. Cut-off was then increased to 45 per cent but, as that only produced more steam which could not get away up the chimney, it was brought back to 40 per cent. By milepost 90, the speed had risen to 126 mph (203 km/h) and the regulator was closed and the brakes applied; in two miles (3.2 km) the speed had come down to 70 mph (113 km/h), but the centre big end had gone, as on *Silver Fox*, so the train was worked slowly back to New England shed. The previous record of 125 mph (202 km/h) had been beaten—but only just, and only momentarily, and it has never since been attempted.

These two high-speed runs of 27 August 1936 and 3 July 1938 indicated that some form of protection was needed to prevent big end failures. This was achieved by using the cavity in the centre crankpin, into which was inserted a metal cylinder containing a glass bulb filled with amyl-acetate. This was calculated to rupture at a temperature of 160°F, the resulting smell warning the driver that trouble was impending. The fact that the crankaxle was of the build-up type enabled this fitting to be more easily adopted.

The problem with this centre bearing was more prevalent on the A.4 class by reason of the enclosing valence plates, and the maintenance of these bearings was the chief headache in the running sheds. The original bearings were of brass with pockets of white metal, which had to be hand-scraped using blueing paste until only minute spots of that could be seen. The fitters called it the 'gnat crap' finish, and it could take several hours of patient toil, working from below in a pit with pretty

crude facilities. A running shed was never a pleasant place in which to work, with open doors at the end in all weathers and with large vents in the roof to let the smoke out.

An early shot of Kings Cross shed shows it to have been of the semi-round type, not a true round house with a central turntable. The Holbeck shed at Leeds was one of those, but they were rare in the UK; there are still plenty in the USA and in Canada.

1939 was the last year that the LNER could really call its own since it was soon to be under government control and then subject to Nationalisation. By the beginning of that year it had 114 Pacific locomotives in service, of which 52 were of the A.1 category, 27 of the A.3 and 35 of the A.4 types. There was also the former No 10000, which had an A.4 boiler and had been converted to the three-cylinder arrangement with Gresley Valve gear. The five North Eastern Pacifics, Nos 2400–4, had been withdrawn in 1936/7 after one No 2404 had been fitted with an A.1 boiler. The A.1 fleet was in the process of conversion to the A.3 type with the fitting of

220-lb (99.8 kg) boilers.

Of the 22 corridor tenders built, one had been fitted to No 10000 and all the rest transferred to the A.4 class. There were three other types of tender, the original GNR type, the new-type non-corridor and the streamlined non-corridor, all of the 5,000-gallon (22,730-litres) capacity; the first two held eight tons of coal and the corridor and streamlined non-corridor held nine tons. The numbers in 1939 were:

GN Type	52
New non-corridor	23
Streamlined non-corridor	18
Corridor	22
	115

Little of interest happened operationally in 1939 since the maximum possible improvement had been applied to the passenger services and the accent was on preparation for war, which was obviously coming. The railways were well equipped to cope with the loads and problems that would be imposed, particularly in so far as the locomotives of the LNER were concerned.

War and Post-War 1939-1947

Compared with the previous four years of glory, these eight years present a very different story. Starting with the outbreak of war on 3 September 1939, all high-speed trains were taken out of service and the A.4 locomotives stored at main line sheds until 4 December, when they were urgently needed. They were then restored to duty, which consisted of hauling anything from freight trains to huge passenger trains of up to 850 tons (863.6 tonnes).

One of the earliest recorded heavy weight runs was that of 31 March 1940. A.1 No 2569 *Gladiateur* had to cope with 16 coaches from Newcastle to Darlington, then with 19 coaches to York and finally 22 coaches weighing in all 750 tons (762 tonnes) to Peterborough, where the load was further increased to 850 tons (864 tonnes) and taken on by a V.2 class, No 4800. The train finally arrived 99 minutes late, but out of that only 9 minutes were attributed to the A.1 and 9 minutes to the V.2. There were around 1300 passengers for the last piece of the journey and steam heating was kept going throughout, though how much reached the tail-end cars is not recorded.

On other occasions, the times with 850-ton trains were recorded as 102 minutes for a V.2 and 96 minutes for an A.1, from London to Peterborough. No 2545 *Diamond Jubilee* did the same journey with 720 tons (731.5 tonnes) in 89 minutes. In April 1940, No 2509 *Silver Link*, the first A.4, took 25 coaches unaided out of Kings Cross, having to start with the engine actually in the Gasworks tunnel where the rails were probably wet. It took 16 minutes for the first 2.6 miles (4.18 km), contending with lots of wheelspin,

but it made the run to Grantham in 123 minutes at an average of 50.2 mph (80.8 km/h).

In February 1941, Doncaster produced Gresley's last design, a lightweight 2-6-2 class V.4 named *Bantam Cock*, incorporating design features of both the V.2 and the A.4 classes. That locomotive, together with a new electric Bo-Bo locomotive No 6701 built for the service between Manchester and Sheffield, was shown to the LNER Directors and the Press at York by Sir Nigel Gresley. That was his last public function and he died on 5 April 1941 after a short illness. Just before then, he would have been pleased to see that his former Assistant, Oliver Bulleid, who had gone to the Southern Railway in 1937, had just produced his first Pacific locomotive in February 1941; that one was numbered 21C1 and was named *Channel Packet*.

Sir Nigel Gresley was succeeded by Edward Thompson, who made it clear from the outset that he was not to be bound by the 'Gresley Tradition'. He did not like the design of the Gresley conjugated valve gear and as a former North Eastern Engineer, with family ties to Sir Vincent Raven, he wanted to make some changes. The wartime conditions of heavy loads, poor fuel and inadequate maintenance had resulted in many troubles due to the mechanism of the three-cylinder locomotives, but these very conditions made it difficult to come up with any satisfactory solution.

Thompson's plans included 10 standard types of locomotive, one of which was to be a mixed traffic Pacific with 74-in (188-cm) diameter driving wheels similar to the new 'Merchant Navy' class on the Southern. In order to produce a prototype for

that class, he rebuilt one of Gresley's Mikados, No 2005, as a 4-6-2 with three separate sets of valve gear. These six Mikados, the class P.2, produced as a 2-8-2 for service in Scotland, had not proved all that was expected of them; most of the time there was not enough traffic to justify their power, besides which they got a reputation for rail-spreading and were often coming off the rails in and around the running sheds.

Just before this planned rebuilding of No 2005, there was an air raid on the City of York on 29 April 1942, just as the 10 pm from Kings Cross arrived in the station with a load of 20 coaches. The locomotive and 14 of the coaches were got away and the station staff managed to save property, furniture and the money from the booking office by stuffing it into gum boots. The horses were all rescued from burning stables, but at the running shed the A.4 Pacific No 4469 was damaged beyond repair. In 1939 it had been renamed *Sir Ralph Wedgwood* in honour of his knighthood; the name was later transferred to No 4466, formerly *Herring Gull*, which later became BR No 60006.

In January 1943 No 2005 was rebuilt as a Pacific by the removal of the leading coupled wheels and the substitution of a bogie in place of the former pony truck. This resulted in a long smokebox with the cylinders behind the bogie, so as to use the short connecting rods previously used on the P.2 class. The three cylinders were 20 in (50.8 cm) diameter by 26 in (66 cm) stroke and the three sets of Walschaerts valve gear drove 10-in (25.4-cm) diameter valves with a travel of 6.75 in (17.1 cm). The boiler pressure was 225 lb per sq in with a firegrate area of 50 sq ft (4.7 m²) and the tractive effort was 40,138 lb (18,206 kg); it carried a classification A.2/2.

That should have provided a good locomotive with the apparent Gresley faults eliminated, but it was not to be so. That engine, together with the other five rebuilds of the original P.2 class, were sent back to Scotland, but did not perform well. They were prone to slipping and the frames proved to be weak at the front end; there may have been local prejudice at the rather ugly rebuild and before long they were sent back to York or Peterborough. They had a poor record for maintenance and reliability, making on average two visits to workshops every year until their withdrawal in 1959. They were numbered 501 to 506, later BR 60501 to 60506, and carried their original names.

The following year (1944) saw the building of another mixed traffic version classified as A.2/1. There were four of these, numbered 3696 to 3699, and they were similar to the A.2/2 except for having smaller cylinders at 19 in (48.3 cm) diameter and a smaller firegrate area, back to the 41.25 sq ft (3.8 m²) of the A.3. These were later numbered 507 to 510 and finally 60507 to 60510. These four were put together from components originally intended for the last of the V.2 'Green Arrow' 2-6-2 class and were fitted with the B.1 bogie, which

Pacific Class A.2/2, rebuilt from Mikado Class P.2 in 1943.

did not ride as well as the Gresley design at high speed though not really intended for that purpose.

After these four came the prototype for a new A.1 Pacific with 80-in (203-cm) diameter wheels and, to produce this in wartime conditions, Thompson decided to use the components of the original No 1470 *Great Northern*. The result of that rebuild, classified A.1/1 and numbered 113 (later 60113), aroused considerable controversy among railway engineers and enthusiasts and was considered almost a sacrilege. Like the other rebuilds, it had its cylinders behind the bogie and was fitted with a double stove-pipe chimney with smoke deflector shields. The boiler pressure was raised to 250 lb per sq in and the three cylinders were 19 in (48.2 cm) diameter with 10 in (25.4 cm) piston valves operated by three sets of Walschaerts gearing. All might have been forgiven if that rebuild had proved itself superior in operation, but like the other A.2 versions it was no better than the A.4 class and again did not ride as well at speed. The trouble probably lay in the long pipe-work involved, due to the location of the cylinders, and under the conditions then prevailing there would not have been time to do any development work on these.

In 1945 the war came to an end, but the railways had barely

recovered when they were faced with the prospect of Nationalisation with all its uncertainties, just as happened after the 1914/18 war. The railways emerged from their wartime efforts with the usual Government treatment, as a result of which, out of profits earned during 1941/5 of £350 million, the Government took £176 million; the incoming Chancellor of the Exchequer referred to them as 'A poor bag of assets'. A different opinion described their efforts as 'The greatest achievement in railway transportation in the history of the world'. The 1442 express locomotives of the LNER, including the 114 Pacifics, had certainly earned their keep during those years.

Edward Thompson retired in June 1946, just as his last design, No 500, had been completed and carried his name. That was only the twelfth Pacific of his build (or rebuild), unlike Gresley who had to wait for the hundredth before he saw his name on it. With a change of Chief Mechanical Engineer there came once more a change in policies, this time with a reversion to the Doncaster line of thought as befitted a former trainee from those works. The A.2 design was modified so as to return the cylinders to lie over the bogie, resulting in a shorter wheelbase and a better appearance due to a shorter smokebox. Fifteen locomotives were built to that design, numbered 525 to 539, and the first

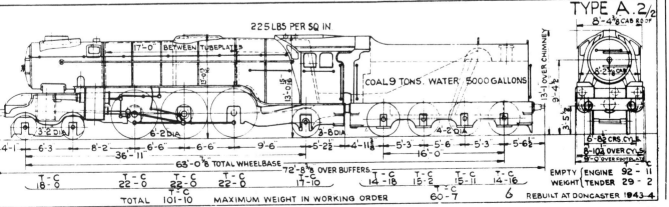

TYPE A.2/2

225 LBS PER SQ IN.

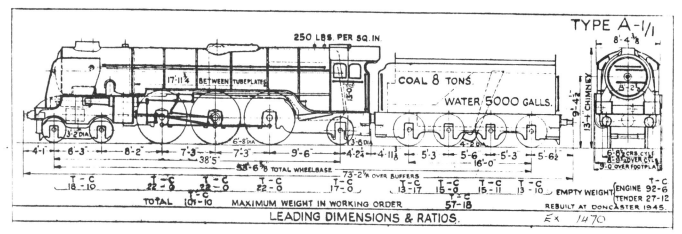

TYPE A-1/1

250 LBS. PER SQ. IN.

17-11¾ BETWEEN TUBEPLATES

COAL 8 TONS.

WATER 5000 GALLS.

13 CHIMNEY

38'5"

6'-8"DIA

53'-6⅝ TOTAL WHEELBASE

73'-2⅛ OVER BUFFERS

EMPTY WEIGHT {ENGINE 92-6 {TENDER 27-12

REBUILT AT DONCASTER 1945.

TOTAL 101-10   MAXIMUM WEIGHT IN WORKING ORDER   57-18

LEADING DIMENSIONS & RATIOS.   Ex 1470

carried the name of the new C.M.E., A. H. Peppercorn. Peppercorn's last design in his capacity as the last Chief Mechanical Engineer of the LNER was that of the final version to carry the A.1 classification, originated in 1923. This was based on the E.T. rebuild of No 1470 in that it had the 80-in (203-cm) driving wheels, 250-lb (113-kg) boiler and three cylinders 19 in by 26 in (48.2x 66 cm). He also retained the separate sets of valve gear for each cylinder. Though designed before Nationalisation, they did not come out before vesting day

of 1 January 1948 and so strictly belong to the category of BR locomotives. There were 49 of these built, numbering at first from 114 to 162, the last being named *Saint Johnstoun*.

From 1939 till the end of 1947 all the Gresley Pacifics had been hard at work and all had come through except No 4469, lost in the air raid on York. By the end of 1947 all the A.1 class had been converted to the A.3 category, with the exception of the rebuilt *Great Northern*. They had their problems, mainly due to the valve gear and the associated big end troubles, but without

Weight diagram of Pacific Class A.1/1 rebuilt from No. 1470.

them the LNER would have been hard-pressed to cope with its wartime loads without having to resort to double-heading.

At the end of 1947 the LNER steam locomotive stock comprised 6,425 tank and tender engines and the number of classes had been reduced from 236 in 1923 to 151. That included 152 Pacific locomotives, compared with 50 on the LMS and 90 on the Southern of that wheel arrangement.

Great Northern, as rebuilt by Edward Thompson and renumbered No. 113, later to be BR 60113.

British Rail Steam Era 1948-1968

On vesting day, 1 January 1948, the newly appointed Member for Mechanical and Electrical Engineering to the Railway Executive section of the British Transport Commission was Mr. R. A. Riddles, formerly Assistant to the Chief Mechanical Engineer of the LMS Railway. One of his problems was to select the best types of locomotive for retention in service and to decide whether to build more of these or to initiate some completely new designs. For that purpose some interchange trials were run during 1948, in which the Gresley Pacifics competed with those of the other 'Regions', as the former railways came to be known, and with the other Pacifics of their own Region.

The former Big Four were divided, on Nationalisation, into six Regions, the extra ones being one for Scotland and what was left of the former LNER being divided into two, called the Eastern and the North Eastern Regions. Later these two were to merge once more, but initially the former C.M.E. of the LNER, A. H. Peppercorn, was responsible for both Regions.

In 1946 Edward Thompson had produced a report on locomotive performance which showed that the A.4 Pacifics were more economical than the various rebuilds produced to that time, so Peppercorn chose three of these A.4s for the trials. The three chosen were *Mallard*, still numbered 22 under Thompson's renumbering scheme; *Sea Gull* (No 60033) and *Lord Farringdon*

(No 60034), all fitted with the Kylchap double chimney. These tests, which were carried out using all the BR dynamometer cars, were run from Kings Cross to Leeds, from Paddington to Plymouth, from Euston to Carlisle and from Waterloo to Exeter. They were all run with train weights around 500 tons (508 tonnes), but to slow post-war schedules averaging 50 mph (80.4 km/h).

Mallard, which had been chosen against advice from Kings Cross shed, which obviously had the best knowledge of its condition, failed on its first run on the Western Region and had to be replaced by *Sea Gull*,

which itself failed on its first run on the Southern Region. Again *Mallard* was substituted, but suffered from a big end failure on 9 June.

In spite of these failures, the A.4s put up the best performance in fuel and water consumption. Following these trials, which took place between April and June 1948, a new locomotive testing plant was opened at Rugby on 19 October. Sir Nigel Gresley had been one of the chief campaigners for such a plant, following the testing of his P.2 *Cock o' the North* on the French installation at Vitry-sur-Seine, and had it not been for the war it would have been operational much sooner. Though Sir Nigel could not be there, the locomotive bearing his name, by then No 60007, was present and indeed was the first one to be set up on the test rollers that same

		Coal lb/HP-hr	Water lb/HP-hr
LNER	A.4	3.06 (1.38 kg)	24.3
LMS	Duchess	3.12 (1.41 kg)	27.1
LMS	Royal Scot	3.38 (1.53 kg)	25.8
GWR	King	3.57 (1.61 kg)	28.6
SR	Merchant Navy	3.60 (1.63 kg)	30.4

The actual coal consumption figures for the A.4 contestants over the different route came to:

		Coal lb/mile
60033	*Sea Gull*, Paddington—Plymouth	42.4 (19.2 kg)
60034	*Lord Farringdon*, Kings Cross—Leeds	39.0 (17.6 kg)
60034	*Lord Farringdon*, Euston—Carlisle	41.1 (18.6 kg)
60033	*Sea Gull*, Waterloo—Exeter	41.4 (18.7 kg)

A.3 Pacific No. 60042 (2507) with single chimney on Scottish Tours Express at Monktonhall Junction. Note the BR logo on the tender.

day. In addition to the new plant at Rugby, the 1904 test plant at Swindon had been rebuilt to take full power outputs and there were three dynamometer cars as well as the three-car mobile loading set, built by the former LMSR, with which to carry out the testing and development of steam locomotives. The result of all this testing was rather inconclusive and resulted in the building of 1,538 locomotives of the former railway types as well as 999 of the new standard British Railway classes numbered 2 to 9. The former figure included 14 class A.2 and 49 class A.1 of the LNER types, as well as one LMS Pacific and 50 of the Bulleid Pacifics of the Southern. The new British Rail standard Pacifics included 10 class 6, 55 class 7 and one class 8.

The non-stop Flying Scotsman was restored to service on 31 May 1948, but taking 7 hours

A.1 Pacific No. 60049 (2548) *Galtee More*, rebuilt as A.3 with Kylchap double exhaust on down express near Hatfield.

50 minutes (50 mph) to do the journey. On 12 August the East Coast line was cut in 10 places by fierce storms and seven bridges were destroyed; as a result the Flying Scotsman was diverted via the Waverley route, making the daily run into 408.6 miles (657.5 km). That run was actually achieved 16 times non-stop until the normal route was restored to service. Those duties were shared between 60029 *Woodcock* and No 22 *Mallard*.

In 1951 the non-stop run to Scotland was taken over by the 'Capitals Limited' express, leaving Kings Cross at 09.30 and doing the run in 7 hr 20 mins. Also that year an event of greater significance for the Gresley Pacifics was the transfer of Kenneth Cook from Swindon to Doncaster, as part of the BR scheme of interchange of Engineers. There he promptly set

about reorganising the repair work and installed an optical lining-up method as used at Swindon, for ensuring that the cylinders and axles were true; as a result, the joints of the conjugated valve gear could be assembled with greater accuracy and with far less clearances in the joints. He also introduced a connecting rod of increased section in which the bearing had a fully-machined white metal finish which did not require hand scraping and in which the clearance was maintained by the use of shims, which could be adjusted in the running sheds. These modifications made all the difference to the Gresley Pacifics; running was smoother and the big end problems virtually disappeared. The distances run between major overhauls for the former LNER Pacifics then became:

A.1	(Peppercorn)	93,363 miles	(150,249 km)
A.2	(Thompson)	85,671	(137,870 km)
A.3	(Gresley)	83,574	(134,496 km)
A.4	(Gresley)	86,614	(139,388 km)

It also reduced their time spent in the sheds and repair shops, as well as improving their reliability in service. For the next ten years the Gresley Pacifics were given a new lease of life and worked all the main East Coast trains, including the new non-stop 'Elizabethan' which first ran on 29 June 1953. That train ran the 392.7 miles (632 km) in 405 minutes that year, reducing the time to 390 minutes the following year.

The next item of note was the arrival of the 2,000-hp diesel-electric locomotive No D.201 at Hornsey shed in April 1958. In June that year, the Flying Scots-man was diesel-hauled for the first time, but the performance of these diesel locomotives was not up to that of an A.4, as was shown in a test run on the down 'Talisman' when times were taken on the ascent from Peter-borough to Stoke Box with a 325-ton (330-tonnes) train. The times and speeds were as fol-lows:

A.4 No. 60006 (4466) *Sir Ralph Wedgwood*, the second A.4 to carry that name after 4469 was wrecked in an air raid at York. Here it is at Potters Bar with the Tees-Tyne Pullman.

	Type 4 Diesel Electric	A.4 Pacific
Peterborough to Stoke Box 23.7 miles	21 min 41 sec	19 min 27 sec
Maximum speed	77.5 mph (125 km/h)	90 mph (145 km/h)
Minimum speed at summit	63.5 mph (102 km/h)	74 mph (119 km/h)

The next year, however, the Eastern Region obtained the use of the prototype 'Deltic' loco-motive, rated at 3,300 hp, and that showed what could be done by going up to Stoke Box at 100 mph (161 km/h). This was all part of the 'Modernisation Plan' which commenced on the Eastern Region in November 1957 with the arrival at Stratford of the first of the Brush 1,250-hp diesel-electrics. In 1958 that Region ordered 22 Deltic diesel-electric locomotives so as to enable a speed-up of the East Coast services to be put into

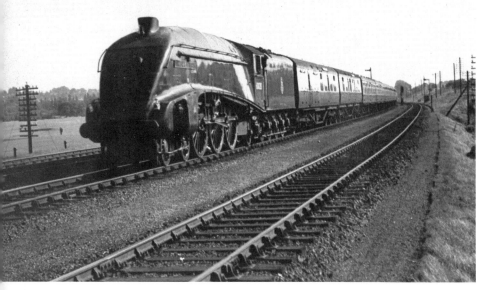

A.4 60028 (4487) *Walter K. Wigham*, on 'Heart of Midlothian' at Potters Bar.

effect. These Deltic locomotives were delivered between March 1961 and May 1962, during which time the Gresley Pacifics had begun to be withdrawn from traffic.

The 10 Thompson rebuilds to classes A.2/1 and A.2/2 had been withdrawn in 1959, as well as one of the A.3 class No 60104 *Solario* (originally 1473), the first of the genuine LNER Pacifics.

The full laying-off rate was as follows:

	A.3	A.4	A.1	A.2
1942 (Air raid)		1		
1959	1			
1961	7			
1962	12	5		
1963	35	10		11
1964	21	7	23	11
1965	2	6	26	1
1966	1	6		7
TOTALS	79	35	49	30

The last to be laid off in September 1966 were a couple of the A.4 highfliers named *Bittern* and *Kingfisher*, their numbers being 60019 (4464) and 60024 (4483). Several of the earlier A.1 class achieved over two million miles and the record is claimed to have been that of No 1475 (60106) *Flying Fox*, which ran over 2.6 million miles or 63,400 miles (102,000 km) per annum.

Before the end of the steam era in 1968, a number of special runs were arranged for the Gresley Pacifics, including that on 27 September 1953 when No 60014 (2509) *Silver Link* the first of the A.4 class, hauled the 'Plant Centenarian', which was run to celebrate the centenary of the opening of the works at Doncaster.

On 23 May 1959 the Stephenson Locomotive Society chartered a Jubilee Special from Kings Cross to Doncaster, hauled by *Sir Nigel Gresley*, then No 60007, and driven by Bill Hoole. That run (which is captured on an Argo record, ZTR 108) got up to 101 mph (162.5 km/h) on the down journey near Hitchin, and on the return up journey a speed of 112 mph (180.2 km/h) was achieved at Little Bytham on the downhill grade from Stoke Box. That was probably the last recorded run of a Gresley Pacific at over 100 mph.

In April 1967 the same loco-motive, officially withdrawn and restored to its original No 4498, took the 'Border Limited' train of 385 tons (391 tonnes) north from Crewe and within 10 miles (16 km) was up to 96 mph (154 km/h). From Carnforth it climbed the 914 ft (278.5 m) to Shap summit, covering the 31.4 miles (50.5 km) in 30 minutes and producing an estimated output of 1,705 drawbar hp.

Superb $2\frac{1}{2}$-in gauge model of an A.1 Pacific built in 1932.

The last A.1 in Service. No. 60052 *Prince Palatine* at St. Margaret's.

That was a fair average for an A.4, but higher outputs have been calculated from timed performances, the highest being 2,380 hp at 80 mph (129 km/h) with a 415-ton (422 tonnes) train.

In 1968, just before the cessation of all steam working on BR, the Flying Scotsman made a special non-stop run to celebrate the 40th Anniversary of its first non-stop run in 1928. To achieve this, the locomotive No 4472, then recently purchased from BR by Alan Pegler, did the journey with a 250-ton (254 tonnes) train. By that date there were only three sets of water troughs still in working order, at Scrooby, Wiske Moor and at Lucker, otherwise the run would have been impossible. The intervening distances between these troughs were then 146 miles (235 km), 74 miles (119 km), 97 miles (156 km) and then the final 76 miles (122 km) to Edinburgh. This put the first stretch beyond the capacity of the 5,000-gallon (22,730 litres) tender, so an additional tender was used purely for water, with a capacity of 6,000 gallons (27,276 litres). On the journey only 1,000 gallons (4,546 litres) were picked up at Scrooby, so that the supply was down to under 2,000 gallons at Wiske Moor, but fortunately those troughs had been refurbished in 1951 and over 3,000 gallons were collected there. With a further 1,000 gallons picked up at Lucker, the run was just completed, but it was touch and go. An empty tender on the main line could have been disastrous as by then there were almost no other filling points left. Even *The Times* got the story wrong and reported in its issue of 2 May that, 'Thirsty Scot stops to drink'. It certainly drank, but it did NOT stop.

Preservation and Models

One way of preserving things that have endeared themselves in the public eye is by means of models and there are plenty of models of the Gresley Pacifics made over the last sixty years.

It was natural that with the appearance of such a good-looking locomotive some models were soon available, and probably the first of these was an 'O'-gauge version built by the Leeds Model Company which they were advertising by December 1922. That was a fine replica 19 in (48.2 cm) long and would be a real collector's piece if any are still available.

Starting in 1925, the Romney, Hythe & Dymchurch Railway in Kent had three working replicas built for their 15-in (38.1-cm) gauge track by Davey Paxman Ltd of Colchester, the first of which was named *Green Goddess*. These are still in use, to the delight of many holiday-makers in that area of Kent. There were also enthusiasts who liked to build their own working versions and a favourite size was to the scale of 1/24 which suited a 2.5-in (6.4-cm) gauge track and in which the driver could sit on the tender.

As soon as the 'OO' gauge began to be popular, Hornby produced a model of the A.4 in 1938 which is still available under the Wrenn label. Triang also produced a model of the A.3 type, numbered 4472, and an A.4 in LNER form with skirts or in BR form without skirts. The latter is of *Mallard* and carries the number 4468 or 60022. Hornby Minitrix offer an A.4 in the 'N' gauge.

Full Size Preservations

In addition to the models, there are five of the A.4 class and one A.3 preserved, some of them still in active service. The most famous and the most travelled of these is the A.3 No 4472 *Flying Scotsman*. The histories of these six are as follows:

1. Flying Scotsman A.3 No 4472

This was first withdrawn from revenue service in January 1963, then carrying the number 60103, when it was purchased by Mr. Alan Pegler, who organised the Fortieth Anniversary run of the non-stop Flying Scotsman train in 1968. He purchased a spare tender to overcome the water problem, since by that time BR were eliminating their watering installations, and he also purchased a spare boiler, which is the main problem in keeping elderly steam locomotives in service.

Following the 1968 run to Edinburgh and back, it was sent to the Hunslet Engine Works at Leeds for an overhaul in preparation for a tour of the USA. That tour was intended to sponsor British business interests and the complete train of nine coaches was equipped for that purpose. It landed at Boston on 28 September 1969 and was assembled and ready for a trial run on 3 October, which took it to New London via Providence and Mystic River, a round journey of 240 miles (386 km). The fuel used was Southern West Virginian coal and No 4472 steamed perfectly well on that. The tour commenced on 7 October 1969 with a 220-mile (354-km) run to New Rochelle, where the fire was drawn for its passage through New York.

From New Rochelle the whole train was towed by a Penn Central electric locomotive, No 4857 of their superb GG1 class, to Hudson Yard, five miles (8 km) south of New York, where steam was raised once more. The tour continued through Baltimore, Washington, Atlanta, Dallas and Fort Worth, finishing up at Houston. The whole train then ran from Houston to Slaton on 19 November and went into winter storage.

During 1970 the tour commenced once more in the Spring and No 4472 paid visits to Kansas City, St Louis and then to the National Railway Museum at Green Bay, Chicago. From there a short detour was made to Canada, with visits to Toronto, where it called at the Spadina roundhouse to meet another steam colleague, and then to Montreal. The return to the USA was made through Detroit and then to Chicago for the Winter.

1971 took it to San Francisco, where after 45 modifications it was allowed to work trains with

15-in gauge version built for the Romney, Hythe & Dymchurch Railway by Davey Paxman in 1925.

Flying Scotsman No. 4472 at the Hunslet engine works before its journey to the USA.

fare-paying passengers on the San Francisco Belt Railroad from 18 March. The vacuum brake caused some puzzlement to the Americans, who were used to the compressed air brake only, but after some explanation it was accepted. The operation was carried out on soft Utah coal, which took some getting used to. At first the consumption was coming to 5 tons (5.08 tonnes) in 30 miles (48 km) with huge quantities of black smoke, which was not very popular, but the technique was mastered in time.

From then on things began to go wrong financially and unfortunately in October Mr. Pegler was declared bankrupt in London. No 4472 then made its way to Stockton, California, where it spent the winter. Long negotiations resulted in the whole outfit being purchased by Mr. W. H. McAlpine and, after the debts had been settled, it set sail from Oakland, California, to arrive in Liverpool in February 1973. On 19 February No 4472 steamed to Derby, where it was overhauled and repainted in time for a visit to an Open Day at Tyseley, Birmingham, on 2 June. From there it went to Didcot on 1 July and thence to the Torbay Railway for the summer season, returning to winter at Market Overton.

During 1974 No 4472 paid visits to many parts of the UK, starting with a run to Bletchley and Hereford in March. On 6 April it ran from Newport to Shrewsbury and by that time the spare tender had been painted to match the BR coach stock colours. Visits to other localities included Leeds, York, Scarborough, Carlisle, Newcastle, Liverpool and Manchester. There were also runs to Ravenglass from Carnforth and BR summer

specials, as well as S.L.O.A. week end tours. That year also saw a visit to an exhibition at Olympia Station in West London and a permanent move to the Steam-town Museum at Carnforth, Lancs.

The next year included a journey to Shildon for the 150th Anniversary of the Stockton & Darlington Railway, followed in 1976 by a centenary run on the Settle to Carlisle line in conjunction with the LNWR 'Hardwicke' of 1895 fame, which Gresley probably saw at Crewe on 22 August of that year.
In 1977 the activities of No 4472 included a part in the Warner Brothers' film *Agatha* and on 30 September 1978 it was one of three steam locomotives which took part in a tribute journey called 'The Lord Bishop' in honour of the late Right Reverend Eric Treacey MBE, formerly Lord Bishop of Wakefield, a railway enthusiast and photographer of renown. That event was followed by an overhaul at the Vickers' works at Barrow, where most of

the Sulzer diesel engines had been built for British Rail.

Two events of note during 1980 included the Rocket 150 Celebration exhibition at Rainhill in May, followed by the Liverpool Road Station exhibition at Manchester in August. A new tender was built by the Wakefield Skill Centre in 1982 and used for a 60th birthday run from Carnforth to Leeds in February 1983, followed by several runs between Peterborough and York.

2. Sir Nigel Gresley A.4 No 4498 (BR No 60007)

The next best known of the preserved Pacifics is No 4498, which was the 100th Gresley Pacific, built in 1937 and withdrawn from revenue service in February 1966, having run 1.8 million miles. It was saved from scrapping and kept at first at the National Coal Board's works at Philadelphia, Co. Durham.

In 1973 No 4498 called first at Carnforth in June on its way to a BR Railfair at Morecambe in August, from where it returned to Philadelphia. It also went to the

No. 4472 *Flying Scotsman* at Carnforth after overhaul at Derby.

150th Anniversary Celebration of the Stockton & Darlington in 1975 and worked on the East Coast Mainline from Sheffield to Newcastle.

In 1977 it had a complete overhaul with retubing of the boiler and then moved to its present home at Steamtown Museum, Carnforth. It has worked on the Cumbrian Coast and Cumbrian Mountain Excursions, the North Yorkshireman and the Scarborough Spa Express. In 1980 it attended the Rocket 150 Celebrations at Rainhill in May and at Manchester in August. It was withdrawn from service in October 1982 for its seven-year boiler overhaul and is now back in service in April 1984.

3. Dwight D. Eisenhower A.4 No 4496 (BR No 60008)

This locomotive was built in September 1937 as No 4496 and named *Golden Shuttle*, being one of two built for the 'West Riding Limited' streamlined train introduced that year. During the 1939/45 war, the locomotive was allocated to a special train built for the use of Field Marshal Eisenhower as Commander-in-Chief of the Invasion Force of 1944. In September 1945 the locomotive was renamed in his honour and on withdrawal in July 1963 it was refurbished and shipped to the American National Railway Museum at Green Bay, Chicago, USA.

4. Union of South Africa A.4 No 4488 (BR No 60009)

Originally built in June 1937 as No 4488, this was one of the five locomotives finished in a special two-tone blue livery intended for the 'Coronation' high-speed streamlined train between Kings Cross and Edinburgh. Withdrawn in May 1966, it was purchased by Mr. J. B. Cameron and preserved on the Lochty Private Railway near St Andrews in Fife. It was the last steam locomotive to be overhauled at the Doncaster Works of the former Great Northern Railway in November 1963. It was almost the last A.4 to be withdrawn.

5. Dominion of Canada A.4 No 4489 (BR No 60010)

This was the first of the five A.4s built for the 'Coronation' high-speed train being produced in May 1937; the other four all came out in the following month. Withdrawn in May 1965, it was overhauled and repainted at Doncaster and then shipped to Canada for a permanent home in the Montreal Railway Historical Museum.

6. Bittern A.4 No 4464 (BR No 60019)

Built in December 1937, No 4464 was the last Gresley Pacific to be withdrawn in September 1966. It was then purchased by the President of the Yorkshire Spastic Society and stored for some time at the National Coal Board's Walton Colliery at Wakefield, Yorks. It was cleared for the working of the BR-approved steam routes from 1976 to 1979 and operated between York and Leeds. In 1979 it was transferred to the Railway Museum at Dinting near Glossop, where it now has its home.

No. 4498 *Sir Nigel Gresley* on turntable at Carnforth Steamtown.

Specifications

TABLE I

Dimensions of Pacific Locomotives, 1907-1922

Railway	GWR	GNR	NER
Built at	Swindon	Doncaster	Darlington
Date built	1907	1922	1922
Locomotive number	111	1470	2400
Locomotive name	*The Great Bear*	*Great Northern*	*City of Newcastle*
Wheel arrangement	4-6-2	4-6-2	4-6-2
Driving wheel diameter (in/cm)	80/203.2	80/203.2	80/203.2
Steam pressure lb per sq in	225	180	200
Heating surface (sq ft/m²)	3154/293	3455/320.9	2874/266.9
Firegrate area (sq ft/m²)	41.8/3.88	41.2/3.82	41.5/3.85
Firetube length (ft/m)	22.5/6.8	19/5.79	21/6.4
Cylinders (ins/cm)	(4)15×26/38×66	(3)20×26/51×66	(3)19×26/48×66
Tractive effort (lb/kg)	27,800/12,610	29,835/13,533	29,918/13,570
Piston valve diameter (in/cm)	8/20.3	8/20.3	8.75/22.2
Piston valve travel (in/cm)	6.88/17.47	4.56/11.58	4.59/11.65
Drawbar HP	860	960	960
Axle load (tons/tonnes)	21/21.3	20/20.32	20/20.32
Total weight (tons/tonnes)	142.8/145	148.8/151	148.1/150.4

TABLE II

Standard dimensions of LNER Gresley Pacifics and No 10000

	A.1	A.3	A.4	W.1
Date built	1922	1928	1935	1929
Built at	Doncaster	Doncaster	Doncaster	Darlington
First number	1470	2743	2509	10000
Name	*Great Northern*	*Felstead*	*Silver Link*	—
Driving wheel diameter (in/cm)	80/203	80/203	80/203	80/203
Steam pressure lb per sq in	180	220	250	450
Cylinders (in/cm)	(3)20×26/50.8×66.04	(3)19×26/48.2×66.04	(3)18.5×26/46.9×66.04	(2)12×26/30.4×66.04 (2)20×26/50.8×66.04
Heating surface (sq ft/m²)	3455/320.9	3398/315.6	3325/308.8	2126/197.5
Grate area (sq ft/m²)	41.2/3.82	41.2/3.82	41.2/3.82	35/3.25
Tractive effort (lbs/kg)	29,835/13,533	32,910/14,927	35,455/16,082	32,000/14,515
Valve diameter (in/cm)	8/20.32	8/20.32	9/22.8	
Travel (in/cm)	4.56/11.5	5.8/14.7	5.8/14.7	
Axle load (tons/tonnes)	20/20.3	22/22.3	22/22.3	22/22.3
Locomotive weight (tons/tonnes)	92.4/93.8	96.2/97.7	103/104.6	103.6/105.25
	All converted to 220 lb/sq in boilers with Kylchap exhaust	All later fitted with Kylchap exhaust blast pipes		Later rebuilt as three-cylinder with A.4 boiler

TABLE III

Gresley Pacifics

THE A.1 CLASS

GNR No	Name	LNER No	Date Built	BR No	Date Condemned
1470	Great Northern	4470	4/22	60113	11/62
1471	Sir Frederick Banbury	4471	7/22	60102	11/61
1472	Flying Scotsman**	4472	2/23	60103	1/63
1473	Solario	4473	3/23	60104	12/59
1474	Victor Wild	4474	3/23	60105	6/63
1475	Flying Fox	4475	4/23	60106	12/64
1476	Royal Lancer	4476	5/23	60107	9/63
1477	Gay Crusader	4477	6/23	60108	10/63
1478	Hermit	4478	6/23	60109	12/62
1479	Robert The Devil	4479	7/23	60110	5/63
1480	Enterprise	4480	8/23	60111	11/62
1481	St Simon	4481	8/23	60112	12/64
	Melton	2543	6/24	60044	6/63
	Lemberg	2544	7/24	60045	11/64
	Diamond Jubilee	2545	8/24	60046	6/63
	Donovan	2546	8/24	60047	4/63
	Doncaster	2547	8/24	60048	9/63
	Galtee More	2548	9/24	60049	12/62
	Persimmon	2549	10/24	60050	6/63
	Blink Bonny	2550	10/24	60051	11/64
	Prince Palatine	2551	11/24	60052	1/66
	Sansovino	2552	11/24	60053	5/63
	Manna*	2553	12/24	60054	6/64
	Woolwinder	2554	12/24	60055	9/61
	Centenary	2555	1/25	60056	5/63
	Ormonde	2556	1/25	60057	10/63
	Blair Athol	2557	2/25	60058	6/63
	Tracery	2558	2/25	60059	12/62
	The Tetrach	2559	3/25	60060	9/63
	Pretty Polly	2560	3/25	60061	9/63
	Minoru	2561	5/25	60062	12/64
	Isinglass	2562	6/25	60063	6/64

NORTH BRITISH LOCOMOTIVE COMPANY BUILD

	Name	LNER No	Date Built	BR No	Date Condemned
	William Whitelaw*	2563	7/24	60064	9/61
	Knight of the Thistle	2564	7/24	60065	9/64
	Merry Hampton	2565	7/24	60066	9/63
	Ladas	2566	8/24	60067	12/62
	Sir Visto	2567	8/24	60068	9/62
	Sceptre	2568	9/24	60069	10/62
	Gladiateur	2569	9/24	60070	5/64
	Tranquil	2570	9/24	60071	10/64
	Sunstar	2571	9/24	60072	10/62
	St Gatien	2572	10/24	60073	8/63
	Harvester	2573	10/24	60074	4/63
	St Frusquin	2574	10/24	60075	1/63
	Galopin	2575	10/24	60076	10/62
	The White Knight	2576	10/24	60077	6/63

THE A.1 CLASS

Name	LNER No	Date Built	BR No	Date Condemned
Night Hawk	2577	10/24	60078	10/62
Bayardo	2578	10/24	60079	9/61
Dick Turpin	2579	11/24	60080	10/64
Shotover	2580	11/24	60081	10/62
Neil Gow	2581	11/24	60082	9/63
Sir Hugo	2582	12/24	60083	5/64

All rebuilt to Class A.3 except No 1470
*Renamed

Name	LNER No	Date Built	BR No	
Prince of Wales	2553	12/26	60054	
Tagalie	2563	7/41	60064	

**Preserved

THE A.3 CLASS

Name	LNER No	Date Built	BR No	Date Condemned
Felstead	2743	8/28	60089	10/63
Grand Parade	2744	8/28	60090	10/63
Captain Cuttle	2745	9/28	60091	10/64
Fairway	2746	10/28	60092	10/64
Coronach	2747	11/28	60093	4/62
Colorado	2748	12/28	60094	2/64
Flamingo	2749	1/29	60095	4/61
Papyrus	2750	2/29	60096	9/63
Humorist	2751	3/29	60097	9/63
Spion Kop	2752	4/29	60098	10/63
Trigo	2595	2/30	60084	11/64
Manna	2596	2/30	60085	10/64
Gainsborough	2597	4/30	60086	11/63
Blenheim	2598	4/30	60087	10/63
Book Law	2599	7/30	60088	10/63
Call Boy	2795	4/30	60099	10/63
Spearmint	2796	5/30	60100	6/65
Cicero	2797	6/30	60101	4/63
Windsor Lad	2500	6/34	60035	9/61
Colombo	2501	7/34	60036	1/64
Hyperion	2502	7/34	60037	12/63
Firdaussi	2503	9/34	60038	11/63
Sandwich	2504	9/34	60039	3/63
Cameronian	2505	10/34	60040	7/64
Salmon Trout	2506	12/34	60041	12/65
Singapore	2507	12/34	60042	7/64
Brown Jack	2508	1/35	60043	5/64

THE A.4 CLASS

Name	LNER No	Date Built	BR No	Date Condemned
Silver Link	2509	9/35	60014	12/62
Quicksilver	2510	9/35	60015	4/63
Silver King	2511	11/35	60016	3/65
Silver Fox	2512	12/35	60017	10/63
Golden Eagle	4482	12/36	60023	10/64
Kingfisher	4483	12/36	60024	9/66
Falcon	4484	2/37	60025	10/63
Kestrel*	4485	2/37	60026	12/65
Merlin	4486	3/37	60027	9/65
Sea Eagle*	4487	4/37	60028	12/62
Union of South Africa**	4488	6/37	60009	6/66
Dominion of Canada**	4489	5/37	60010	5/65
Empire of India	4490	6/37	60011	5/64
Commonwealth of Australia	4491	6/37	60012	8/64
Dominion of New Zealand	4492	6/37	60013	4/63
Woodcock	4493	7/37	60029	10/63
Osprey*	4494	8/37	60003	12/62
Golden Fleece	4495	9/37	60030	12/62
Golden Shuttle*	4496	9/37	60008	7/63
Golden Plover	4497	10/37	60031	10/65
Sir Nigel Gresley	4498	11/37	60007	2/66
Gadwall*	4469	11/37		6/42
Great Snipe*	4462	11/37	60004	7/66
Sparrow Hawk	4463	12/37	60018	6/63
Bittern**	4464	12/37	60019	9/66
Guillemot*	4465	12/37	60020	3/64
Herring Gull*	4466	1/38	60006	9/65
Wild Swan	4467	2/38	60021	10/63
Mallard**	4468	2/38	60022	4/63
Pochard*	4499	4/38	60002	5/64
Garganey*	4500	4/38	60001	10/64
Gannet	4900	5/38	60032	10/63
Capercaillie*	4901	5/38	60005	3/64
Sea Gull	4902	6/38	60033	12/62
Peregrine*	4903	6/38	60034	8/66

Name	LNER No.	BR. No.
*Renamed:		
Sir Ronald Matthews	4500	60001
Sir Ralph Wedgwood	4469	—
William Whitelaw	4462	60004
Sir Murrough Wilson	4499	60002
Sir Charles Newton	4901	60005
Sir Ralph Wedgwood	4466	60006
Andrew K. McCosh	4494	60003
Dwight D. Eisenhower**	4496	60008
Miles Beevor	4485	60026
Walter K. Wigham	4487	60028
Lord Farringdon	4903	60034

**Preserved:
1 Dwight D. Eisenhower: Green Bay, Wisconsin, USA
2 Union of South Africa: Lochty Private Railway
3 Dominion of Canada: Montreal Railway Museum, Canada
4 Bittern
5 Mallard: National Railway Museum, York

POST-GRESLEY PACIFICS

Class A.2/2	LNER	1943 Rebuild	BR Nos
Cock o' the North	2001	501	60501
Earl Marischal	2002	502	60502
Lord President	2003	503	60503
Mons Meg	2004	504	60504
Thane of Fife	2005	505	60505
Wolf of Badenoch	2006	506	60506

Class A.2/1		1944	
Highland Chieftain	3696	507	60507
Duke of Rothesay	3697	508	60508
Waverley	3698	509	60509
Robert the Bruce	3699	510	60510

Class A.1/1		1945	
Great Northern	1470	113	60113

Class A.2/3		1946	
Edward Thompson		500	60500
Airborne		511	60511
Steady Aim		512	60512
Dante		513	60513
Chamossaire		514	60514
Sun Stream		515	60515
Hycilla		516	60516
Ocean Swell		517	60517
Tehran		518	60518
Honeyway		519	60519
Owen Tudor		520	60520
Watling Street		521	60521
Straight Deal		522	60522
Sun Castle		523	60523
Herringbone		524	60524

Class A.2		1947	
A. H. Peppercorn		525	60525
Sugar Palm		526	60526
Sun Chariot		527	60527
Tudor Minstrel		528	60528
Pearl Diver		529	60529
Sayajiro		530	60530
Bahram		531	60531
Blue Peter		532	60532
Happy Knight		533	60533
Irish Elegance		534	60534
Hornet's Beauty		535	60535
Trimbush		536	60536
Bachelor's Button		537	60537
Velocity		538	60538
Bronzino		539	60539

BRITISH RAIL-BUILT, LNER DESIGN

Class A.1		1948
W. P. Allen	114	60114
Meh Merrilees	115	60115
Hal o' the Wind	116	60116
Bois Roussel	117	60117
Archibald Sturrock	118	60118
Patrick Stirling	119	60119
Kittiwake	120	60120
Silurian	121	60121
Curlew	122	60122
H. A. Ivatt	123	60123
Kenilworth	124	60124
Scottish Union	125	60125
Sir Vincent Raven	126	60126
Wilson Worsdell	127	60127
Bongrace	128	60128
Guy Mannering	129	60129
Kestrel	130	60130
Osprey	131	60131
Matmion	132	60132
Pommern	133	60133
Foxhunter	134	60134
Madge Wildfire	135	60135
Alcazar	136	60136
Red Gauntlet	137	60137
Boswell	138	60138
Sea Eagle	139	60139
Balmoral	140	60140
Abbotsford	141	60141
Edward Fletcher	142	60142
Sir Walter Scott	143	60143
King's Courier	144	60144
Saint Mungo	145	60145
Peregrine	146	60146
North Eastern	147	60147
Aboyeur	148	60148
Amadis	149	60149
Willbrook	150	60150
Midlothian	151	60151
Holyrood	152	60152
Flamboyant	153	60153
Bon Accord	154	60154
Borderer	155	60155
Great Central	156	60156
Great Eastern	157	60157
Aberdonian	158	60158
Bonnie Dundee	159	60159
Auld Reekie	160	60160
North British	161	60161
Saint Johnstoun	162	60162

Class W.1	4-6-4 Built 1929	
10000	Rebuilt 1937	60700

The Official NEWCASTLE UNITED Football Club Annual 2016

Written

Designed

Thanks to Amanda Brennan, Michael Bolam and Paul Joannou.

A Grange Publication

© 2015. Published by Grange Communications Ltd., Edinburgh, under licence from Newcastle United Football Club. Printed in the EU.

Every effort has been made to ensure the accuracy of information within this publication but the publishers cannot be held responsible for any errors or omissions. Views expressed are those of the author and do not necessarily represent those of the publishers or the football club. All rights reserved.

Photographs © Serena Taylor, Getty Images and NCJ Media

ISBN 978-1-910199-51-0

CONTENTS

Welcome from Steve McClaren

A very warm welcome to the 2016 Newcastle United annual and what a pleasure it is for me to be writing this foreword as Head Coach of the club.

I'm aware that last season was a very disappointing campaign for everyone associated with the club and it's certainly not where a club of Newcastle United's standing should be. We have set new, and what I believe are achievable, targets this season and you can rest assured that myself, the coaching staff and the players will be 100% focused and hugely motivated to achieve those aims.

Newcastle is a football-mad city and is incredibly passionate. I hope you will see that reflected both in our play this season and in this year's annual.

In bringing the likes of Georginio Wijnaldum, Aleksandar Mitrovic, Chancel Mbemba and Florian Thauvin to the club, we have signalled our intent to get back to the right end of the Premier League. At the same time we're aiming to make an impact in domestic cup competitions, for I know how much they mean to you.

The support this football club receives is phenomenal and as an outsider looking in, as I have been over recent years, it's widely acknowledged up and down the country that the passion and fervour you have for your team is the envy of many.

In this year's annual I've particularly enjoyed reading about some of the great players we have had over the years and the South American influence at the club. Coupled with the behind the scenes features, testing quizzes and other fun segments it really is a super read.

I hope you enjoy reading this year's annual as much as I did and I wish you all the best for 2016.

Steve McClaren
Head Coach

SEASON REVIEW

A SEASON OF UPS AND DOWNS

In many ways the 2014/15 season mirrored that of the previous season, however the fact that United's fate wasn't decided until the last day of the campaign meant it was a nervy end to the season on Tyneside. The Magpies started the season poorly and were even bottom of the pile after four games before picking up and cementing a mid-table position by the New Year. United struggled in the second half of the season and whilst never being in the bottom three places, came perilously close to the dreaded relegation trapdoor. There was though, at times, much to applaud in the Premier League campaign, including exciting victories over Chelsea and Liverpool at St. James' Park and well-earned wins at Tottenham and Manchester City, the latter coming in the League Cup.

Mike Williamson scores against Crystal Palace

AUGUST

United kicked off the 2013/14 campaign against Manchester City and once again, the unforgiving fixture computer handed Newcastle United a first-day fixture against City, who this time came to St. James' Park as Barclays Premier League champions.
The occasion was tinged with sadness as it marked the first game at Gallowgate since the terribly sad loss of supporters John Alder and Liam Sweeney in the horrific MH17 air disaster the previous month. Before the game kicked off wreaths were laid on the centre-circle that included tributes from Sunderland AFC, whose fans contributed over £30,000 to the memorial fund - an astonishing amount.

Back to the action on the pitch and the visitors proved too hot to handle, winning on Tyneside for the fifth season in a row thanks to goals from David Silva and Sergio Aguero. The day saw United debuts given to Daryl Janmaat, Remy Cabella, Emmanuel Riviere and, from the bench, Rolando Aarons and Ayoze Perez. The latter of course would go on to enjoy a terrific breakthrough season for the Magpies. A dour goalless encounter followed at Villa Park before United rounded off their August fixtures by dropping two valuable points against Crystal Palace, the Eagles snatching a draw with an injury-time strike from Wilfried Zaha. Progress was made in the Capital One Cup with a comfortable, albeit single-goal, victory at Gillingham.

SEPTEMBER

After a two-week international break, Newcastle returned to action at St Mary's where Southampton inflicted a second consecutive 4 – 0 defeat on United. The south-coast venue proved a none too pleasant arena for United, with the Magpies 10 – 0 down to the Saints in three games since their promotion back to the Premier League in 2012. Hull City were the next visitors to Tyneside and when Steve Bruce's side opened up a two-goal lead, the natives were getting a tad restless. Cometh the hour, cometh the man and when Papiss Cisse entered the fray with 20 minutes left on the clock, it was left to the Senegalese striker to net twice to salvage a point for United.

In a shortened month, United's third and final league game of September saw Alan Pardew's side travel to Stoke for Sky's Monday Night Football. An early header by Peter Crouch settled a scrappy affair, and the Geordies were left to rue a late miss by Jack Colback that would at least have brought one point home to Tyneside. As it was, United were left second bottom with just Burnley between them and the ignominy of last place. Respite was provided by another League Cup win as United took on Crystal Palace at Selhurst Park, a side they had met only three weeks earlier in the League. Emmanuel Riviere opened his account for United with two goals but Palace struck once again in injury time to force extra time. Local lad Paul Dummett proved United's saviour, diving spectacularly to head in United's winner after Adam Armstrong provided the perfect left-wing cross.

Papiss Cisse celebrates after his equaliser against Hull

United draw level through Papiss Cisse at Swansea

NOVEMBER

Two league wins on the trot was a great boost for players and fans alike, but the visit of Liverpool to Gallowgate would be a stern test. The match at Gallowgate the previous season had been a classic encounter and this game was no different even though it only produced one goal. As both sides battled for supremacy, it was second half substitute Ayoze Perez who capitalised on an error from Alberto Moreno to bury what was only a half chance past the despairing Simon Mignolet and send the stadium into a state of frenzy. United were marching up the table now and after a straightforward three points at the Hawthorns against West Brom, where Perez scored probably what was United's goal of the season, audaciously back-heeling in a Daryl Janmaat cross, the Magpies were up to eighth. The good form continued with a fifth league win in a row as Queens Park Rangers, struggling at the wrong end of the table and eventually bound for relegation, were seen off at St. James' Park, Moussa Sissoko scoring with only 12 minutes left on the clock. November must be one of Alan Pardew's favourite months as the genial Londoner picked up the Barclays Manager of the Month award, having done exactly the same in November 2013. Despite losing the last game of the month at West Ham, the winner coming somewhat fortuitously when a complete miss-hit from Cheikhou Kouyate ended up in the path of Aaron Cresswell who scored his first goal for the Hammers.

OCTOBER

Newcastle kicked off October with a tricky visit to south Wales to face Swansea City. United trailed twice but came from behind on both occasions to earn a well-deserved point, Papiss Cisse on target once again scoring in each half to nullify goals from Wilfried Bony and Wayne Routledge. A win was desperately needed and it was the visit of Leicester City that finally brought United their first three points of the season at the eighth attempt. Gabriel Obertan scored the only goal of the game in a match that will be remembered for its late kick-off caused by problems with the installation of the new giant scoreboard at the Leazes End of the stadium.

Buoyed by that win United then faced a Tottenham side who had been in Europa League action in midweek. With their opponents burdened by that, Newcastle recorded a fine 2 – 1 victory at the Lane, their second consecutive win in N17. Trailing to an Emmanuel Adebayor first-half header, Sammy Ameobi, a second-half substitute, made Premier League history by scoring the fastest goal after the interval in the 23-year history of the league, timed at just under seven seconds. Credit though to Jack Colback, who picked him out with a fine pass right from the kick-off. United's final action of the month saw their great run in the Capital One Cup continue at the Etihad Stadium. In what was probably the shock result of the round, goals from Rolando Aarons and Moussa Sissoko gave United a victory only the most die-hard of Geordies could have predicted.

Ayoze Perez hits the winner against Liverpool

Papiss Cisse stuns Chelsea

DECEMBER

December was to prove a tough month for the Magpies and a very busy one too. League leaders Chelsea were first up at St. James' Park, and for the second year in a row they returned south pointless as two Papiss Cisse goals were enough to earn United a marvellous three points and inflict a first defeat of the season upon Jose Mourinho's men. Rob Elliot started in goal for United but he had to be replaced at half time by rookie Jak Alnwick who did tremendously well on a truly memorable league debut.

Arsenal were too strong for the Magpies a week later at the Emirates, losing 4 – 1, and in the following midweek match, United sadly bowed out of the League Cup, going down 4 – 0 at Tottenham. Next up was the biggest home game of the season against north-east rivals Sunderland. Amid massive disappointment on Tyneside, a last-minute goal from Adam Johnson gave the Wearsiders the points and even worse it was their third successive win at Gallowgate – a nightmare for the Geordies. Defeat at Old Trafford followed on Boxing Day before a morale-boosting end-of-year win against Everton rounded off 2014, with United sat in 10th place in the Premier League and aiming to push on in the New Year.

Speculation was rife at the end of the Everton game that manager Alan Pardew might be ready to up sticks and move to the club where he enjoyed the best days as a player, Crystal Palace. And so it was, three days into the New Year John Carver was confirmed as Pardew's successor as Head Coach for the remainder of the season.

Ayoze Perez nets United's consolation at the Emirates

JANUARY

The first game of the New Year was a third round FA Cup tie at Leicester. Youngsters Callum Roberts and Lubomir Satka made their first appearances for United in what turned out to be a miserable day for the Magpies, losing by a single goal at the King Power Stadium. League Champions-elect Chelsea comfortably beat United 2 – 0 at the Bridge a week later, before surprise outfit Southampton arrived on Tyneside midway through the month. The south-coast side, who were enjoying a particularly good campaign under Ronald Koeman, inflicted a third home defeat of the season on United, winning 2 – 1. United ended the month at the KC Stadium and came up with their most emphatic win of the season, 3 – 0 in what, come the end of the season, would turn out to be an absolutely crucial three points. Remy Cabella scored his first goal of the season and with strikes to follow from Sammy Ameobi and Yoan Gouffran it was a happy United party who boarded the coach home to Tyneside. United had slipped one place to 11th at the end of the month, remarkably a position they would maintain for the next six games.

Handball! And it's no goal for Hull at the KC

A jubilant Steven Taylor does the trick against Burnley

Papiss Cisse earns three points against Aston Villa

FEBRUARY

United should have beaten Stoke in their first home game in February. Jack Colback had given United the lead with only 16 minutes remaining, but not for the first time this season United conceded late in the game, a trait that would cost them valuable points come the end-of-season tot-up of points on the board. This time it was gentle giant Peter Crouch who rose highest of all to head a 90th-minute equaliser – such occasions feeling like a loss for the fans rather than a point won. A reunion with Alan Pardew followed and, not surprisingly, the two sides cancelled each other out in a 1 – 1 draw.

United then suffered their worst defeat of the season, a horrendous five-goal thrashing at the Etihad against Manchester City and it could have been worse, the visitors were three down after only 21 minutes and five down after 53. A crucial game awaited United at the end of the month, the Magpies were on 32 points, 10 ahead of Villa who occupied a position in the bottom three. A win and surely United had done enough to steer clear of any relegation worries? And a win it was, Papiss Cisse scoring the only goal of the game to give John Carver his first home win and send the Geordies home in a happy mood.

Jack Colback peels away after netting against Stoke

MARCH

A shortened month caused by an International break and no FA Cup involvement for United saw the Magpies play only three games. The Black and Whites hosted Manchester United on the first Wednesday in March and it looked like a goalless stalemate until a freak goal right at the death gifted the visitors the three points, Ashley Young profiting from

An aerial dual as Arsenal visit St. James' Park

defensive chaos in the United 18-yard box. Still it was a fighting and encouraging performance by the home side and they travelled to Everton hopeful of picking up another point or three that would virtually assure them of safety. Fabricio Coloccini saw red though and three goals by the hosts easily condemned United to a dispiriting defeat. A week later a stirring second-half display almost brought United a point against Arsenal but the damage had been done in the first half where a brace from Olivier Giroud had opened up a two-goal cushion for Arsene Wenger's Gunners. Moussa Sissoko struck straight after the break, but intense pressure on David Ospina's goal failed to bring a much merited equaliser. United slipped to 12th after this latest defeat but were still 10 points off the third bottom club.

David de Gea keeps Emmanuel Riviere out at St. James' Park

11

Colback is Jack in the Box against Tottenham

APRIL

The much anticipated Tyne-Wear derby at the Stadium of Light turned out to be a damp squib for all associated with Newcastle United and perhaps even worse than that. It was not quite humiliation, as the game was won by a single Jermain Defoe strike, but United failed to deliver a performance – the very least demanded by the supporters.

That was defeat number four in a row and a 2 – 0 reversal at Anfield the following week made it five on the bounce.

Surely successive home games against Tottenham and Swansea would bring an end to that horrendous run? But no, United were in freefall and defeats six and seven swiftly followed despite Siem De Jong getting on the score sheet for United against Swansea in what had sadly been an injury-ravaged season for the popular Dutch signing from Ajax. United ended the month in 14th place in the League, a nervy seven points above the relegation places but still clearly with their fate entirely in their own hands.

A trademark Ayoze Perez celebration against Swansea

MAY

Four games to go and first up were Leicester City who at the beginning of April were three points adrift at the bottom of the league and 16 points behind Newcastle - yet before kick-off they knew a win would elevate them to within one point of the Magpies in the table, quite remarkable. And did they do it? Sadly with surprising ease, to make it eight defeats on the spin for United in a match that they finished with only nine men on the field following the dismissals of Mike Williamson and Daryl Janmaat. Character was needed from John Carver's charges and at last they delivered, ending the run of defeats with a point against West Brom at St. James' Park, Ayoze Perez's strike proving decisive.

Acrobatics from Emmanuel Riviere at Loftus Road

Victory at already relegated Queens Park Rangers on the penultimate weekend of the season would have seen United safe, but after leading at half time through Emmanuel Riviere's first league goal of the campaign, United threw it away in the second half - meaning a final-day showdown with West Ham, in front of millions watching on TV, would seal their fate.

A raucous atmosphere greeted the players as they took to the field and the stadium erupted when Moussa Sissoko headed in Jonas Gutierrez's cross after the break. It was the Argentine, as it transpired playing his final game for the club, who wrapped up the victory with the second goal five minutes from time. United could have lost and still been safe, as Hull failed to beat Manchester United, but it was fitting that United did the business themselves and in fine style too.

Relief as Moussa Sissoko opens the scoring against West Ham

Dream Debuts

New signings, especially strikers, will always hope to do well in their first game for their new club. Here we look at three goal scorers who made their United debuts at St. James' Park, and what a smashing time all three had!

Newcastle United 13 – 0 Newport County, 5 October 1946

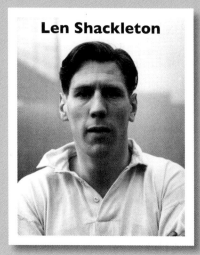

Len Shackleton

Len Shackleton was known as the 'Crown Prince' of football and many who watched him play said they had never seen a player quite like 'Shack' before. He was a complete showman who could perform every trick in the book. With a tremendous record in wartime football, the 24-year-old Shackleton joined United for a record fee after hitting 171 goals in 217 games for Bradford. And what a debut awaited the Yorkshireman at St. James' Park. It was Newcastle's ninth game of the season and after a bright start United were winless in four and needed a morale-boosting win to kick-start their promotion challenge as the south Wales outfit arrived on Tyneside.

Incredibly the Magpies won 13 – 0 (they were seven up at the interval), a Football League record that still stands today. Shack hit a double hat-trick including three goals within five minutes, to make headlines around the country.

The Geordies couldn't keep that sort of form up though, and went on to finish the season in fifth place. Shack departed for arch-rivals Sunderland in February 1948 after falling out with the United hierarchy.

United's team that day included such players as Joe Harvey, Frank Brennan and Jackie Milburn who, of course, would go on to win

promotion the following season and enjoy the Wembley Cup successes of the early 1950s. For the record, United's full list of scorers that day was Shackleton (6), Charlie Wayman (4), Jackie Milburn (2) and Roy Bentley (1).

Newcastle United 5 – 2 Leeds United, 19 August 1989

Mick Quinn

United's last match of the 1988/89 season had been against Manchester United at Old Trafford, but sadly they would be starting the 1989/90 season in Division Two after falling through the relegation trapdoor the previous May. Manager Jim Smith had re-assembled the squad bringing in the likes of Kevin Dillon, Mark McGhee (the second time he'd signed for United) and of course

Mick Quinn, the Liverpool-born natural goal scorer who would form a terrific partnership with McGhee (the two of them hit 61 goals between them that season).

Quinn opened the scoring, shooting past Mervyn Day from the penalty spot, but strikes from Bob Davison and Ian Baird gave Leeds a half-time lead. Quinn was on fire, and he quickly levelled things up after the break before poaching a third to give United the lead once more. John Gallacher, another debutant, made it four, beating Day at his near post before Quinn wrapped it up with probably the best goal of the game.

Leeds were pushing forward for a third goal but Kevin Dillon won the ball midway inside his own half and, in doing so, played it forward to the unmarked Quinn just inside his own half. With the visitors defence nowhere to be seen, Quinn raced towards the Leazes End goal before coolly slotting the ball past the advancing Day and into the bottom left hand corner of the net. That goal marked Quinn out as a scorer of real class, and he would go on to hit 36 that season. Sadly United just missed out on promotion back to the top flight through the play-offs – losing to Sunderland of all clubs!

Newcastle United 3 – 0 Coventry City, 19 August 1995

Les Ferdinand arrived on Tyneside at the start of the 1995/96 season, having been brought from Queens Park Rangers for a hefty £6m fee - a then-record for United. Also making their debuts on a warm summer afternoon were Warren Barton, David Ginola and Shaka Hislop - some talent!

Coventry City were the first visitors to St. James' Park that season, the Sky Blues being an established Premier League outfit in the 1990s and possessing players such as Dion Dublin and John Salako. City had finished 16th the previous season, while the United entertainers side were just evolving after a sixth-place finish the previous campaign.

Sir Les, as he was to become known by the Geordie faithful, proudly took the number

Les Ferdinand

nine shirt and joined a formidable front three also featuring Peter Beardsley and Ginola.

The visitors would have been delighted with an opening day point but United had other ideas and tore into City right from the off, playing a brand of football that would thrill not only Magpie fans but football supporters the length and breadth of the country.

Rob Lee opened the scoring on seven minutes before Beardsley made it two on 82 from the spot. Ferdinand was proving a real handful for Borrows and Williams in the City back four and he capped a splendid all-round performance with the third a minute later. Latching onto a through-ball from Lee, he raced forwards towards the Gallowgate End before rounding keeper John Filan in full flow and knocking the ball into the net from a tight angle, just inside the right hand post to rapturous applause from all four sides of the stadium.

And so the legend that was Sir Les Ferdinand was born. He would go on to make 84 appearances for United scoring 50 goals - a terrific record. Still hugely respected and much loved on Tyneside, Les is now director of football at Queens Park Rangers.

GOING FOR GOAL

Aleksandar Mitrovic, Azoye Perez and Siem De Jong are all trying to score, but only one of them can complete the task – can you work out who will find the net?

Answers on p62.

NUFC MATHS Challenge

A quiz with a difference that not only teaches you about Newcastle United but gets to grips with tricky maths challenges.

Work out the questions below and the answer is the number of a current squad player.

A

The year Newcastle last won the Championship

÷

Age of Papiss Cisse

−

The number of players on a football pitch

=

B

Moussa Sissoko's squad number

+

United's top flight league title wins

x

The number of goals scored by Rolando Aarons in 2014/15

=

C

Clean sheets in the 2014/15 Premier League season

x

The round number that Newcastle reached in the 2014/15 League Cup

÷

Florian Thauvin's squad number

=

D

The number of European goals scored by Alan Shearer

+

United's FA Cup wins

÷

The most famous Newcastle United shirt number

=

E

Premier League goals scored in 2014/15

x

The number of former England managers United have had

÷

Steve Harper's squad number in 2003/04

=

Answers on p62.

Steven Taylor

Who was your boyhood hero?
Tony Adams

What was your best footballing moment?
Scoring my first goal for Newcastle against Celta Vigo at St. James' Park in 2006

Who is your toughest opponent?
Ruud van Nistelrooy

Which team did you support as a boy?
Newcastle United

What's your pre-match meal, and favourite food?
Chicken, pasta and poached egg, and chicken Thai green curry

Do you have any superstitions?
I don't have any

Who is your favourite current player?
John Terry

Who is your favourite person from another sport?
Floyd Mayweather

What's your favourite stadium other than St. James' Park?
The Emirates, Arsenal

What would you be if you weren't a footballer?
Homeless!

Where did you go for your 2015 summer holiday?
Las Vegas

Who's the funniest/daftest player at the club?
Daryl Janmaat

Who is your favourite actor?
Denzel Washington

What is your favourite TV show?
Entourage

What do you like doing in your spare time?
Relaxing with friends

What advice would you give a young player?
Always do that little bit extra

Which three people would you invite round for dinner?
Cheryl Fernandez-Versini, Eva Mendes and Mila Kunis

What's the best thing about being a footballer?
Living your dream

PLAYER Q AND A

Ayoze Perez

Who was your boyhood hero?
Lionel Messi

What was your best footballing moment?
Signing for Newcastle United in July 2014

Who is your toughest opponent?
John Terry

Which team did you support as a boy?
CD Tenerife

What's your pre-match meal, and favourite food?
Pasta, and tortilla española

Do you have any superstitions?
Putting my right boot on first and then touching the grass as I go onto the pitch

Who is your favourite current player?
Zlatan Ibrahimovic

Who is your favourite person from another sport?
Rafael Nadal

What is your favourite stadium other than St. James' Park?
Old Trafford, Manchester

What would you be if you weren't a footballer?
Working in sport somewhere, maybe as a PE teacher

Where did you go for your 2015 summer holiday?
Miami and Tenerife

Who's the funniest/daftest player at the club?
Steven Taylor

Who is your favourite actor?
Vanesa Romero

What is your favourite TV show?
La Que se Avecina, it's a comedy show set in Madrid

What do you like doing in your spare time?
Resting, playing PS4, shopping, bowling

What advice would you give a young player?
Talent is no use without dedication

Which three people would you invite round for dinner?
Pep Guardiola, Xavi and Ronaldo

What's the best thing about being a footballer?
Being able to do what you love

Paul Dummett

Who was your boyhood hero?

Alan Shearer

What was your best footballing moment?

Scoring at the Gallowgate End versus Liverpool

Who is your toughest opponent?

Eden Hazard

Which team did you support as a boy?

Newcastle United

What's your pre-match meal, and favourite food?

Pasta and chicken, and Sunday Lunch

Do you have any superstitions?

I don't have any

Who is your favourite current player?

Ronaldo

Who is your favourite person from another sport?

Lewis Hamilton

What is your favourite stadium other than St. James' Park?

The Emirates, Arsenal

What would you be if you weren't a footballer?

A plumber

Where did you go for your 2015 summer holiday?

Ibiza and Mexico

Who's the funniest/daftest player at the club?

Steven Taylor

Who is your favourite actor?

Liam Neeson

What's your favourite TV show?

Entourage

What do you like doing in your spare time?

Chill out and spend time with my family and friends

What advice would you give a young player?

Ensure your attitude is spot on and learn from your coaches

Which three people would you invite round for dinner?

David Beckham, Mila Kunis and Michelle Keegan

What's the best thing about being a footballer?

Being able to do your favourite hobby as a job

PLAYER Q AND A

Daryl Janmaat

Who was your boyhood hero?

Johan Cruyff

What was your best footballing moment?

Beating Spain 5-1 in the World Cup 2014

Who is your toughest opponent?

Ronaldo

What team did you support as a boy?

Feyenoord

What's your pre-match meal, and favourite food?

Pasta, and Indonesian dishes

Do you have any superstitions?

None

Who is your favourite current player?

Lionel Messi

Who is your favourite person from another sport?

Roger Federer

What is your favourite stadium other than St. James' Park?

Old Trafford

What would you be if you weren't a footballer?

A policeman

Where did you go for your 2015 summer holiday?

Ibiza

Who's the funniest/daftest player at the club?

Tim Krul

Who is your favourite actor?

Liam Neeson

What is your favourite TV show?

Goede tijden, slechte tijden - it's a Dutch soap opera

What do you like doing in your spare time?

Being with my family

What advice would you give a young player?

Enjoy it and always do your best

Which three people would you invite round for dinner?

My wife and two children

What's the best thing about being a footballer?

Being on the pitch and playing in front of thousands of your fans

Three of a kind

A game with a difference...

1. Three teams from London starting with letter C who have played in the Premier League?

2. Three teams to score four against United in 2014/15?

3. Three players who have scored the most Premier League goals for United?

4. Three players who have won the most international caps whilst at United?

5. Three players with their surname starting with N to have played for United in the Premier League?

6. Three teams United beat away from home in 2014/15?

7. Three players starting with surname S who played in the 1999 FA Cup Final for United

And the bonus three questions:

From the answers to your questions above:

1. Which three teams are ever present in the Premier League?

2. Which three players also played for Aston Villa?

3. Which three players have scored in penalty shoot-outs for Newcastle?

Answers on p62.

Quiz 1

Let's see what you remember about the 2014/15 season!

1. Who scored United's first goal of the season?

2. Who knocked United out of the FA Cup?

3. Which team scored the most goals (7) against United?

4. Which four teams did United score three goals against in the League?

5. Which United player was the first to be sent off (in August)?

6. How many clean sheets did United keep in the League, 4, 8 or 12?

7. Who left United in January 2015 for Inter Milan?

8. Which two teams did United fail to score against last season?

9. Which two players debuted in the FA Cup for United but are yet to play in the Premier League?

10. United played one game on a Thursday in 2014/15, against whom?

Quiz 2

See how much you know about Newcastle United past and present!

1. Why is the date 11th June significant in United's history?

2. Who were Newcastle's first Premier League opponents in 1993?

3. Les Ferdinand, Wayne Routledge and Loic Remy all have connections with which other team?

4. Who played in the 1924 FA Cup Final for United and managed them in 1951, winning on both occasions?

5. Who were United's only League Cup semi-final opponents in 1976?

6. Who was United's goalkeeper in the 1974 FA Cup Final?

7. What colour shirts did United wear when they beat Sheffield Wednesday at home in September 1993?

8. Which Spanish club did Jonathan Woodgate play for?

9. Who were United's last European opponents?

10. Who is the only Paraguayan to play for United in the Premier League?

Answers on p62.

FA CUP AND LEAGUE CUP REVIEWS

FA CUP ROUND-UP

Round 3: Leicester 1 – 0 Newcastle United

The FA Cup is a competition that is famous around the world and, when the final comes around in May, it is one of the most celebrated days in English football. Newcastle last won the Cup in 1955 against Manchester City and have been beaten in three finals since then: 1974 against Liverpool, 1998 against Arsenal, and 1999 against Manchester United.

Newcastle drew Leicester City in the third round at the King Power Stadium. Unfortunately for United it was the seventh time in the last nine seasons that they had been drawn away in the third round, a bit unlucky with the FA Cup numbered balls to say the least! United had gone out in the third round for the past two seasons and sadly it was to be an unwanted hat-trick for the Magpies.

Leonardo Ulloa's header separated the sides in what was a scrappy affair with clear-cut chances few and far between. Remy Cabella saw a first-half effort harshly ruled out for offside, while Adam Armstrong and Haris Vuckic threatened for the Magpies after the break. At the other end, United goalkeeper Jak Alnwick produced two excellent saves to deny substitutes Chris Wood and Marc Albrighton. John Carver handed Lubomir Satka and Callum Roberts debuts from the bench but Newcastle were unable to salvage anything from the contest.

So another season of disappointment in the FA Cup, six third-round exits in the last nine seasons and no fifth-round appearance since the 2005/06 season. Hopefully 2015/16 will bring much needed Cup joy to Tyneside.

LEAGUE CUP ROUND-UP

Round 2: Gillingham 0 – 1 Newcastle United
Round 3: Crystal Palace 2 – 3 Newcastle United
(after extra time)
Round 4: Manchester City 0 – 2 Newcastle United
Round 5: Tottenham Hotspur 4 – 0 Newcastle United

Newcastle United do not have fond memories of the League Cup having only managed to reach the final on one occasion in its 54-year history, losing to Manchester City in 1976. Although there was no success in this year's competition Newcastle could hold their heads high after a good run to the quarter-finals.

The Magpies started the competition in round two with an away trip to Gillingham, the first time they had played the Gills since another League Cup meeting back in 1976 and it was a repeat performance, with United coming out on top again thanks to a single Gabriel Obertan strike.

It was back to south-east London for round three and with United heading for victory at Crystal Palace, a last minute goal from the hosts levelled things and forced extra time. United weren't to be denied, and it was left to Paul Dummett to spectacularly head the winner eight minutes from time.

The draw was not kind to Newcastle once again as they pulled out Manchester City at the Etihad in the fourth round. Alan Pardew's side defied the odds and in a hugely impressive performance, goals from Rolando Aarons and Moussa Sissoko deservedly saw United through.

Sadly, the quarter-final was a step too far for United, going down 4 – 0 at Tottenham in a game they were never really in. Spurs went on to reach the final but lost 2 – 0 to Chelsea at Wembley.

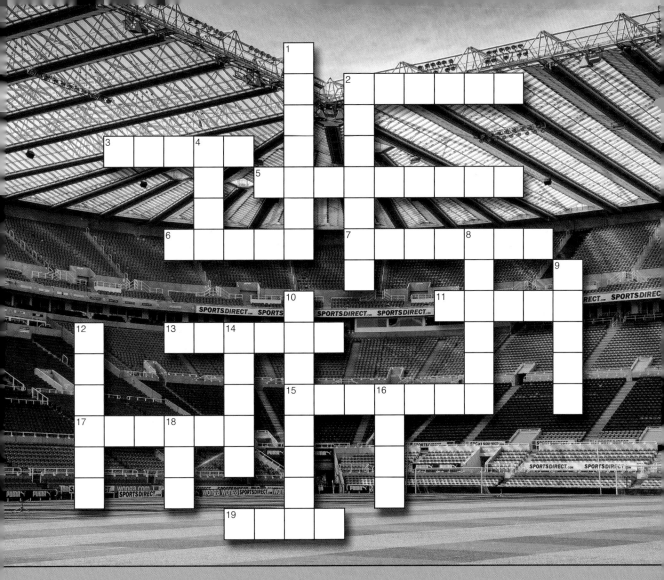

ACROSS

2. Chipped it over Schmeichel (6)
3. Giuseppe and Italian goal scorer (5)
5. The legendary Hughie (9)
6. Also played for Leeds and Blackburn (5)
7. Left-back Olivier (7)
11. Signed from Spurs in 1998 (5)
13. Newcastle-born defender in the 90s (6)
15. Greek defender (7)
17. Long-serving United centre-half (6)
19. Scored 40 goals for England (4)

DOWN

1. Welsh striker, partnered Shearer (7)
2. Brothers Matty and Ritchie (7)
4. On-loan French striker from 1999 (4)
8. Wore number 16 in 2014/15 (6)
9. United's man from Tenerife (5)
10. Signed from Leeds, sold to Real Madrid (8)
12. French defender with Everton in 2014/15 (6)
14. Centre-half signed from Wimbledon in 1988 (5)
16. Captain Jim from the 1960s (4)
18. The General (3)

Answers on p62.

SPOT THE DIFFERENCE

Can you spot the ten differences in this match between Newcastle and Liverpool?

Answers on p62.

THE NAME GAME

Can you match the nationality to these 20 United players from around the world?

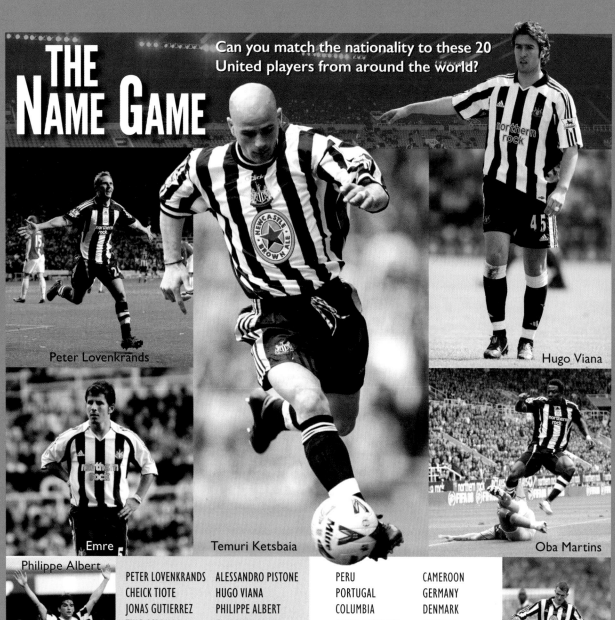

Peter Lovenkrands

Hugo Viana

Temuri Ketsbaia

Emre

Philippe Albert

Oba Martins

PETER LOVENKRANDS	ALESSANDRO PISTONE	PERU	CAMEROON
CHEICK TIOTE	HUGO VIANA	PORTUGAL	GERMANY
JONAS GUTIERREZ	PHILIPPE ALBERT	COLUMBIA	DENMARK
TINO ASPRILLA	CLARENCE ACUNA	CZECH REPUBLIC	GEORGIA
EMRE	ANDREAS ANDERSSON	ITALY	CHILE
NOBBY SOLANO	DIEGO GAVILAN	GREECE	IVORY COAST
MARK HOTTIGER	TEMURI KETSBAIA	SWEDEN	BRAZIL
NIKOS DABIZAS	DIDI HAMANN	NIGERIA	ARGENTINA
PAVEL SRNICEK	GEREMI	BELGIUM	PARAGUAY
CACAPA	OBAFEMI MARTINS	TURKEY	SWITZERLAND

Didi Hamann

Nikos Dabizas

Pavel Srnicek

Alessandro Pistone

Answers on p62.

A Look
Back in Time

We looked at the 1990s and 2000s in the 2015 annual, so this time we're jumping back in history to look at two very exciting periods in United's past. First it's the Edwardian era, before we move on to the 1920s later in the Annual.

The 1900s – Edwardian Dominance

United dominated English football in the Edwardian era, the years covering the reign of King Edward VII from 1901 to 1910. The period was undoubtedly the most successful of United's long and illustrious history. And what a pleasure it must

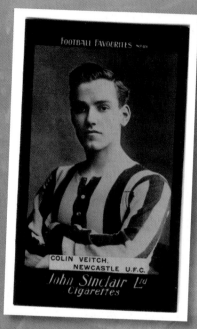

Jimmy Howie

have been to be a United fan during that time!
When King Edward VII came to the throne in January 1901 after the death of Queen Victoria, Tyneside was a thriving industrial city and its football team was ready to embark on a ten-year period of dominance. In 1900/01 United finished 6th in the first division as they looked to build on their recent promotion to the top flight three years earlier. Managed by a committee rather than a single figurehead, United were bringing top quality signings to St. James' Park such as Scots Andy Aitken, Jimmy Howie and Ronald Orr to compliment local lads like Colin Veitch, Jack Carr and Jack Rutherford - all of whom would go down in history as true United greats.

In 1901/02, 14 clean sheets from Matt Kingsley helped United finish third in a season that included an 8 – 0 win over Notts County. The following year was a

bit of a blip. United were in the bottom half of the table, but notably beat Sunderland at Gallowgate for the first time, Bob McColl scoring, in a result that denied the Wearsiders the League title. 1903/04 saw the Magpies challenge for the title for the first time, they were second going into the final month of the season and were to become renowned for their slick football - a brand of short-passing in a possession style that would be their hallmark in the seasons ahead.

And so to 1904/05 and the first of United's three titles in five seasons. Seven wins in a row propelled them to the top of the table by Christmas and despite losing their final home game to Sunderland, wins at Sheffield Wednesday and Middlesbrough on the final day secured the Championship. Jimmy Howie was United's top goal scorer with 17, followed by Bill Appleyard on 15. It could have been a 'double' too, but United lost the Cup Final to Aston Villa.

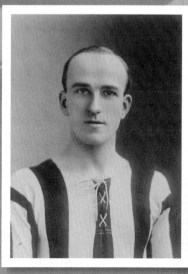

Jack Rutherford

The 1905 Cup Final Team

The following season the Champions only won one of their first seven games, but recovered to finish fourth and reach another Cup Final. September 1905 was also notable for the opening of a substantially remodelled St. James' Park with a capacity of over 60,000.

And so to another league success in 1906/07. United were second or third for the first part of the season, but after beating Arsenal at St. James' Park in January, they took over top spot and never relinquished it. United won 18 of their 19 home games and drew the other in a remarkably consistent season on Tyneside.

United were again amongst the frontrunners in 1907/08, but lost their last two games to Middlesbrough and Sunderland to slip from second to fourth in the final standings. It was yet another Cup Final defeat for the Geordies to bear – at their bogey ground, Crystal Palace, where it was said the pitch didn't suit their short-passing game.

1908/09 brought the third Championship success, achieved despite an incredible 9 – 1 home loss to Sunderland in December where the half time score was only 1 – 1! United lifted the title with a record 53 points (remember it was only two points for a win in those days, today it would have been equivalent to 77 points).

And so the decade was brought to an end with an FA Cup success at last. United finished fourth in the league again but defeated Barnsley 2 – 0 in a replayed final played at Goodison Park, Albert Shepherd scoring twice.

It's worth looking at the full record of United during this period as it makes hugely impressive reading, bar season 1902/03:

Edwardian Summary:

Season	League	FA Cup
1901/02	3rd	QF
1902/03	14th	1
1903/04	4th	1
1904/05	1st	F
1905/06	4th	F
1906/07	1st	1
1907/08	4th	F
1908/09	1st	SF
1909/10	4th	W
1910/11	8th	F

(Round 1 in the 1900s is equivalent to round 3 today)

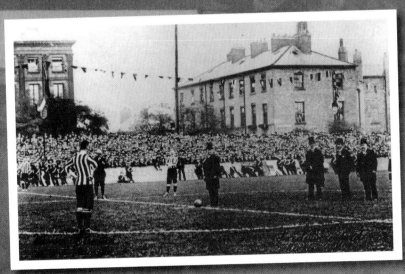

Edwardian St. James' Park

SOUTH AMERICAN TANGO

Faustino Asprilla

VENEZUELA

GUYANA

SURINAME FRENCH GUIANA

Fumaca

COLOMBIA

ECUADOR

Nolberto Solano

PERU

BRAZIL

Mirandinha

George Robledo
Ted Robledo

BOLIVIA

Cacapa

CHILE

PARAGUAY

Diego Gavilan

Fabricio Coloccini

ARGENTINA

URUGUAY

Ignacio Gonzalez

Clarence Acuna

Daniel Cordone
Jonas Gutierrez
Christian Bassedas

UNITED'S
SOUTH AMERICANS

players over the years, starting from George and Ted Robledo back in 1949 right
up to Fabricio Coloccini in the present day. All in all, United have had 14 of them
on their books. Here we profile them all. Some have been huge successes, some
flamboyant and others simply frustrating. Read on...

George ROBLEDO, **Chile**

Born: Iquique, Chile on 14 April 1926
Played: 1949 – 1953
Debut: v Charlton Athletic (H)
5 February 1949
Appearances: 166
Goals: 91
International Caps: 31

Ted ROBLEDO, **Chile**

Born: Iquique, Chile on 26 July 1928
Played: 1949 – 1953
Debut: v Aston Villa (A)
31 December 1949
Appearances: 47
Goals: 0
International Caps: 9

A deadly goal-getter, Chilean-born George formed an outstanding forward line with Jackie Milburn and Bobby Mitchell, a trio that scared defences up and down the country. He had an English mother, and was actually brought up in Yorkshire after the family had emigrated from South America following the Chilean revolution in 1932. Prior to his move to Newcastle, George was a pit worker in Wath and played as a 15-year-old in Barnsley's war-time side. He was a grafter, working hard for the team, and was lethal in front of goal whenever an opportunity came his way. Team-mate Mitchell paid him a great compliment saying, 'He used to blast them in from all directions and they went like a bullet'. During 1951/52 he equalled Hughie Gallacher's scoring record of 39 goals and was Division One's leading scorer. A Cup winner in 1951 and 1952, he netted the winner against Arsenal in 1952. One of United's most popular players of the era, George was also the first United player to play in the World Cup Finals.

The younger of the two Robledo brothers, Ted's career followed much the same path as his more famous counterpart. A makeweight in the deal that brought George to Gallowgate, Ted became a valued squad player and earned a regular position in midfield during season 1951-52. Honest and hard-working at left-half, he was a steady performer rather than brilliant and rivalled Charlie Crowe for a place in United's engine room. He took part in all the FA Cup ties leading to Wembley in 1952, and won a cup winners medal in the 1 – 0 Wembley success over Arsenal alongside brother George who scored the winner. Ted returned to Chile at the end of the 1952/53 season playing for top club Colo-Colo and also won international honours alongside George. His untimely death in 1970 was shrouded in controversy, having been reported missing overboard from a tanker in the Persian Gulf. After an Interpol investigation, the West German captain of the boat was arrested for his murder.

Born: Fortaleza, Brazil on 2 July 1959
Played: 1987 – 1990
Debut: v Norwich City (A)
1 September 1987
Appearances: 67
Goals: 24
International Caps: 4

Born: Tulua, Colombia on 10 November 1969
Played: 1996 – 1998
Debut: v Middlesbrough (A)
10 February 1996
Appearances: 63
Goals: 18
International Caps: 57

Coming from a family of eight children, as a youngster Mirandinha worked down a salt mine before joining his first club, SC Maguary, as a 14-year-old. Moving on to Palmeiras, he was the first Brazilian to take to the field at the top level in England. He became United's record purchase at £575,000, a move that was seen by some as being speculative and risky. He scored over 300 goals in Brazil, where he was also the owner of a pig farm in Sao Paulo, before bringing his talents to Tyneside. Mira, as he was nicknamed, had an explosive pace over 10 yards and possessed a powerful shot. Mira (full name Francisco Ernandi Lima) could be electrifying and frustrating at the same time. He linked superbly with the emerging Paul Gascoigne but another colleague, John Hendrie, said you needed two balls on the pitch - one for Mira and one for the rest of the team! Nevertheless he was a popular character on Tyneside, and after returning to his homeland in 1990 enjoyed more success with Palmeiras before taking on various coaching roles.

Flamboyant, highly talented, a maverick – just some of the words used to describe the Colombian international when he arrived on Tyneside for a record £7.5m from Italian side Parma. Tino had a unique style and a special ability to bamboozle defenders, with manager Kevin Keegan saying he was 'a one-off, a special player and a big-stage performer'. An entertainer, he also specialised in an acrobatic somersault celebration that delighted supporters. Unorthodox, Tino had deceptive pace and could call on an array of extravagant ball skills. A touch erratic, his crowning moment on Tyneside was his hat-trick against Barcelona in the Champions League in September 1997. Both fabulous and frustrating, he returned to Parma after two years in England after making United one of the most talked about clubs in the country. He spent his retirement breeding horses as well as appearing on Colombian television celebrity shows and more conventional football programmes.

Played: 1998 – 2004 & 2005 – 2007
Debut: v Chelsea (A)
22 August 1998
Appearances: 315
Goals: 48
International Caps: 95

Played: 1999 – 2000
Debut: v Tottenham Hotspur (H)
28 November 1999
Appearances: 6
Goals: 0

Reputedly Peru's highest-paid sportsman of all time, Nobby became the first Peruvian to play in England when he came to Newcastle via Boca Juniors of Argentina in August 1998. A slight but skilful ball-player Nobby, who quickly became a crowd favourite, was a dead-ball expert and first class crosser who created countless chances from wide positions. He earned a glittering reputation at an early age in Peru where he started his career as an amateur with Alianza Lima. He joined Sporting Cristal in 1992 and in 1997 moved across South America to join Boca Juniors of Argentina – and his idol Diego Maradona. Scorer of over 50 goals in seven seasons in South America, and capped at the early age of 19 for Peru, Nobby went on to play 95 times for his country. He scored what he described as 'the best goal of my career' when he notched United's first goal in the 3 – 2 Intertoto Cup win at 1860 Munich in July 2001. Now Assistant Coach to the Peru National Team, he helped guide his country to the semi-finals of the 2015 Copa America.

Brazilian midfielder Jose Antunes, known in the South American way by his playing name 'Fumaca', arrived in England in 1998 with the aim of securing a professional contract. Playing in the Brazilian second division for AD Catuense, he then earned short term deals with Colchester United and Crystal Palace before getting his chance with United – largely thanks to Mick Wadsworth, Bobby Robson's right hand man at St. James' Park. Tall, slender and athletic-looking, sadly he didn't display any of the Brazilian magic associated with the more famous footballers of his country, and his career with United did not take off as was hoped. He made only one full starting appearance against Tottenham. He rarely showed his best to the fans and failed to claim a regular place in the Magpies' first-team squad. After nine months on Tyneside he moved on, trying his luck at a succession of clubs around Europe, and eventually playing at a lower level of football in Germany. One that didn't quite work out for United!

Diego GAVILAN, Paraguay

Born: Asuncion, Paraguay on 1 March 1980
Played: 2000 – 2004
Debut: v Sunderland (A)
5 February 2000
Appearances: 8
Goals: 1
International Caps: 43

Clarence ACUNA, Chile

Born: Rancagua, Chile on 8 February 1975
Played: 2000 – 2003
Debut: v West Ham United (A)
28 October 2000
Appearances: 59
Goals: 7
International Caps: 61

Diego was the first Paraguayan ever to play in England. A fast, skilful runner, Diego left his native country behind at the age of 19 in January 2000 to join United. Already capped several times before leaving his teens, Diego quickly broke through into the first team and played six times for Bobby Robson's side in the 1999/2000 season, scoring his first Premiership goal against Coventry in April 2000. Nicknamed 'Sparrowhawk', this son and nephew of famous title-winning Paraguayans was also capped eight times for both the Paraguay Under-17 and Under-20 teams while playing for his only club before Newcastle, Cerro Porteno of Asuncion. During 2000/01, Diego failed to break regularly into the first-team picture and joined Club Autonoma Universidad (Mexico) on loan for the duration of 2002 but returned to St. James' Park in August 2002. Diego played for Paraguay in the 2002 World Cup Finals and joined Sporting Club Internacional, Porto Alegre of Brazil in January 2003 on loan before leaving United. He finished his career in Central and South America.

Clarence was a hard-working Chilean international midfielder capped 59 times (five as captain) for his country. Clarence began his career at O'Higgins in Rancagua where he made his senior debut aged only 15. He joined Newcastle from Universidad de Chile in October 2000 and became the first Chilean to play for United since the Robledo brothers, George and Ted, in the 1940s and 50s. Clarence won three Championships with Universidad, then fulfilled his ambition of playing in Europe when Bobby Robson brought him into the Premiership at the age of 25. During his first season in England, he impressed onlookers with a number of tenacious displays and he opened the 2001/02 season with a goal at Chelsea. But he only made 16 Premiership appearances during that season and four in 2002/03. He excelled at breaking up the play, a spoiler, and would win the ball for the likes of Kieron Dyer and Nobby Solano to 'do their stuff'. On retirement he acted as an advisor for his first club, O'Higgins.

Christian BASSEDAS, Argentina

Born: Buenos Aires, Argentina on 16 February 1973
Played: 2000 – 2003
Debut: v Bradford City (H)
1 November 2000
Appearances: 33
Goals: 1
International Caps: 22

Daniel CORDONE, Argentina

Born: Buenos Aires, Argentina on 6 November 1974
Played: 2000 – 2001
Debut: v Manchester United (A)
20 August 2000
Appearances: 27
Goals: 3

Christian was a major summer purchase prior to the start of the 2000/01 season and was one of Argentina's most accomplished midfield players. He joined his only previous club, Velez Sarsfield, as a 10-year-old and played through all the youth ranks before turning professional in 1991. A veteran of over 300 professional games, he won four Argentinian Championship medals as well as victories in the 1994 Americas Cup and International Cup. He made his national-team debut in 1994 and went on to win 43 full caps, scoring one goal, as well as winning 15 caps at Under-21 and 12 at Under-23 level. A close follower of English football, he was delighted to get the chance to compete in the Premiership at the age of 27. Unfortunately the start to his United career was put on hold due to a broken foot suffered during United's pre-season matches. That injury meant he didn't make his United debut until November 2000, and after that he initially struggled to adapt to the frenetic pace of the Premiership. A signing that looked good business at the time, but one that didn't quite work out for the player and United.

Cordone was spotted by United when they were watching fellow Argentine Christian Bassedas and in his first few games for the Magpies showed United fans that they had unearthed a player of real quality. He scored on his home debut against Derby County in a match that also marked the opening of United's newly enlarged 52,000 capacity stadium. Purchased as forward cover, he operated behind the twin strike force of Alan Shearer and Carl Cort, but got the opportunity to shine when Cort was out injured. Plucky and energetic, Daniel (nicknamed the Wolf) had a rock-star image with his long hair, pony tail, earrings and tattoos. Having spent 10 years at Velez Sarsfield in Argentina, Daniel was unable to build on his early promise and sparkling form, and by the time the 2001/02 season came along he was no longer in Bobby Robson's plans. He returned home in 2002 to join Argentinos Juniors, and had a spell with San Lorenzo, before taking on a coaching role with Deportivo Mutal Leandro. A bit of a wild boy, but he did his bit for United.

CAÇAPA, Brazil

Born: Lavras, Brazil on 29 May 1976
Played: 2007 – 2009
Debut: v Aston Villa (H)
18 August 2007
Appearances: 39
Goals: 2
International Caps: 3

Ignacio GONZALEZ, Uruguay

Born: Montevideo, Uruguay on 14 May 1982
Played: 2008 – 2009
Debut: v Hull City (H)
13 September 2008
Appearances: 2
Goals: 0
International Caps: 18

Caçapa, real name Claudio Roberto da Silva, was a strong and domineering central defender – his ability to do the simple things being the major strength of his game. He signed for United on a free transfer from French Champions Lyon where he was the leader of the Brazilian pack. As club captain for three seasons, he was widely regarded as one of the best central defenders in Ligue 1, demonstrating a solid, powerful, muscular and versatile presence in the heart of the defence. Caçapa joined Lyon from Brazilian side CA Mineiro where he was deployed both at right-back and centre-half in his early days in France. The ferocity of his tackles was respected as widely as the kindness and courtesy he displayed away from the pitch. Caçapa, who won the last of his three caps for Brazil in July 2001, was a bubbly and likeable character who was delighted to be donning a black and white shirt once again, as those were the colours worn by his first club, Atletico Mineiro in Brazil. Caçapa actually became the 1000th player to pull on the black and white shirt when he appeared for United for the first time on 18 August 2007 at home to Aston Villa. After finishing his career on the pitch, he coached the Brazil Under-15s.

Ignacio Gonzalez (known as 'Nacho') joined United on transfer deadline day, 1 September 2008, signing for the Magpies on a one-year loan deal from Valencia. Ignacio began his career in his home country of Uruguay with Danubio (Montevideo) in 2002 and won the Premier Division title with them in 2004 and 2007. In 2008 he moved to Europe, making five 'on loan' appearances for Monaco in the French League and scoring once before signing a permanent deal with La Liga side Valencia. Just as the 2008/09 La Liga season started, 'Los Che' agreed a loan deal with Newcastle before the midfielder had played for the Mestalla-based side. A full international player, Ignacio made his debut for the Uruguay National Team in a 2-1 defeat to England at Anfield in 2006. He won 18 caps and scored his only goal for 'La Celeste' against Japan on 20 August 2008. Sadly he was sidelined with an ankle injury for much of 2008/09 and ended up making only two appearances for the Magpies before joining Greek side Levadiakos. A grafter rather than an entertainer, Nacho returned home to Uruguay in 2013.

Jonas GUTIERREZ, **Argentina**

Born: Roque Saenz Pena, Argentina on 5 July 1983
Played: 2008 – 2015
Debut: v Manchester United (A)
17 August 2008
Appearances: 205
Goals: 12
International Caps: 22

Fabricio COLOCCINI, **Argentina**

Born: Cordoba, Argentina on 22 January 1982
Played: 2008 – present
Debut: v Manchester United (A)
17 August 2008
Appearances: 248
Goals: 6
International Caps: 36

The Argentina international signed from Spanish outfit RCD Mallorca and had the nickname 'Spiderman' for wearing the superhero's webbed mask during flamboyant goal celebrations. Jonas began his career with Velez Sarsfield in Argentina in 2001, helping the club win the Primera Division title in 2005 before moving to Spain. Jonas made three appearances for Argentina in the 2010 World Cup in South Africa and then only missed one league game in each of the 2010/11 and 2011/12 seasons. Jonas joined Norwich on loan in January 2014 for remainder of the 2013/14 season but at the start of the 2014/15 season it was revealed Jonas was battling cancer after being diagnosed with testicular cancer back in 2013. Happily given the all-clear on 4 November 2014, he made an emotional first team return against Manchester United on 4 March 2015. He scored the goal against West Ham which sealed the three points for United on the final day of the 2014/15 season. A very popular and much loved and respected player during his seven seasons on Tyneside.

Fabricio joined United from Deportivo La Coruna in August 2008. He began his career with the youth team of Argentinos Juniors but made his professional debut in 1998 with Boca Juniors. The following season he moved to AC Milan but spent most of his five years at the San Siro out on loan before moving to Deportivo. In 2004 Coloccini was an Olympic Gold medallist with Argentina in Athens where his team-mates included Carlos Tevez and Javier Mascherano. In the 2006 World Cup in Germany, Fabricio played twice for Argentina, against Holland and Germany. In 2007/08 he played every minute of Deportivo's La Liga campaign, the first player to do so since the 1999/2000 campaign, before joining United. Colo was also voted into the PFA Championship team of the season in 2009/10 before being named as United's club captain for the 2011/12 season. He was also voted North East Football Writers Player in 2011. A proud member of the PFA Team of the Season for 2011/12, a few injuries limited his time on the pitch in 2013 but back to his imperious best in 2013/14 and captain again in 2015/16.

Behind the Scenes: The Newcastle United Medical Room

Pre-season is one of the busiest periods at the Newcastle United Training Ground. In early July the players report back for training and undergo various medical and physical tests to check their levels of conditioning after the summer break. Once they're completed, many of the players go into the physio room for treatment or a pre-training massage from one of the club's dedicated medical team.

Below we illustrate a typical day at United's Benton base.

Here is physio Michael Harding working on Fabricio Coloccini's leg muscles.

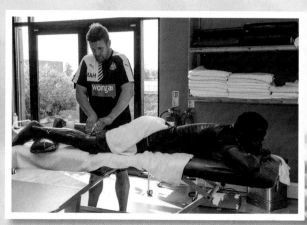

Masseur Mick Holland is making sure Cheick Tiote's calf muscles are in good shape.

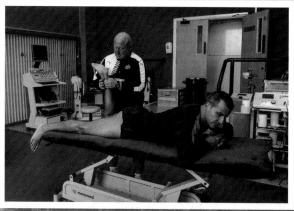

Head physiotherapist Derek Wright checks that Steven Taylor is raring to go.

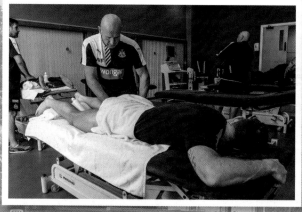

Masseur Wayne Farrage gets to grips with Mike Williamson's hamstrings.

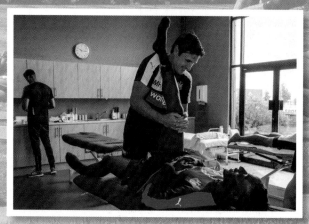

A bit of flexibility work for Massasio Haidara with Michael.

It's not all about rubs and stretches; the paperwork has to be completed too. Wayne is making sure it's all spot on.

Strength and Conditioning coach Chris Wilding works with Mehdi Abeid and Daryl Janmaat in the gym.

Michael Harding looks on as the players get ready for some serious leg work.

After all the hard work behind the scenes it's onto the training pitch to do what they all love – football!

But before they're finished, the players come off the training pitch and do a series of warm down stretches under the watchful gaze of fitness coach Alessandro Schoenmaker and Chris Wilding.

SPOT THE BALL

Can you spot the ball in this match between Newcastle and Arsenal?

Can you spot the ball in this match between Newcastle and Swansea?

Answers on p62

WORDsearch

Find the words in the grid. Words can go horizontally, vertically and diagonally in all eight directions.

```
L R C A M N O T H G U O H T N
Z E O F R X R J T K G Q M L H
Z K L K L D F O S W G F H Q B
C E E R R Q N W E R G A N E D
M N K A N R E A U D M R L K L
A I V P A D V B X P E D P N A
R L T F E M N C D E D R O P N
A X I N R E L E G A L S H C O
D F X Q T X N R W E P A D G D
O K E T S B A I A M R L F C C
N P A L J F M Z I T B M L C A
A L R P H K N S D H S D A L M
C N O S G D O H V M N R T N Z
X C O L O C C I N I C V U L Y
T E C H N O L O G Y C Z P H X
```

The 20 word search names are all from these 20 clues:

Newcastle's stadium - St. James' ... (4)

1980s United winger Chris ... (6)

Introduced in 2014 - Goal-line ... (10)

2014 World Cup Winners ... (7)

Argentinian Star from 80s Diego ... (8)

Scotland's National stadium ... Park (8)

England Manager - Roy ... (7)

League One Team Crewe ... (9)

Gary ... From Match of the Day (7)

Football's World Governing Body ... (4)

United's Captain in 2015/16 - Surname ... (9)

Former United manager - Glenn ... (6)

Andy or Ashley or Carlton ... (4)

2015 European Under 21 Champions ... (6)

England Women's captain - Steph ... (8)

Scored a hat-trick in 1966 World Cup Final - Geoff ... (5)

Supermac - Malcolm ... (9)

United Coach Paul ... (7)

Top referee - Mark ... (11)

United's Georgian from the 1990s - Temuri ... (8)

A Look
Back in Time
The 1920s

We looked at the 1990s and 2000s in the 2015 annual, so this time we're jumping back in history to look at two very exciting periods in United's history. The 1900s were covered earlier in the Annual, so here we focus on the 1920s.

The team pictured in London in 1927

The roaring 20s was a period of sustained economic prosperity, and it was reflected in society and also in football. The National Stadium, Wembley, opened in 1923 and, as we'll discover, United were soon to be acquainted with the world-famous ground. The war years (1914 – 1918) had demoralised people, but sport, and football in particular as the national sport, was back with a bang. Everton, Liverpool and Huddersfield

Town, the Terriers on three occasions, lifted the League Championship during the 1920s, whilst United began the decade with a solid fifth-place finish.

United spent heavily in the transfer market at the start of the decade, with the likes of Neil Harris and Tom McDonald arriving from Partick Thistle and Rangers respectively. The Magpies spent most of the season in second or third place, helped by an October double over Sunderland (United won the fixture at St. James' Park 6 – 1), but two wins out of their last eight games meant they slipped down the table at the end of the season. The following season United flattered to deceive and it turned into a mid-table campaign with only a strong finish of four wins in the last five games, catapulting them up to seventh. This season, 1921/22, also marked the final curtain for Jimmy Lawrence, who ended his 15-season and 19-year association with the club. In 1922/23 United once again

pushed for the upper reaches of the division. They were top after two games, but inconsistent away form (they took almost twice as many points at St. James' Park as on their travels) cost them dearly, and a fourth place finish was the best they could achieve. A year on, and whilst it was a ninth place finish at the end of the season, United had the honour of playing in only the second FA Cup Final to be played at Wembley. United met Aston Villa in the Cup Final and, as a quirk of fate, they also faced them a week earlier at Villa Park in a dress rehearsal for the big day. United played a shadow squad to save their players for the Final, and duly paid for that by losing 6 – 1, but when it mattered, in front of a 100,000 all-ticket crowd, United won 2 – 0 with goals from Stan Seymour and Neil Harris – the Wembley fairytale had begun for United! Moving into the 1924/25 season United were once again a well-respected side and even managed to lead the table with five games left

Frank Hudspeth

although they came through that dip in form, they ended up in ninth come the end of the season. The League Champions had for some inexplicable reason not performed as they might have.

The Championship side broke up in 1928/29 and the season was a largely disappointing one with three late wins propelling them up from 12th to 10th as the curtain came down on the end of a decade that had been, all

1920s St. James' Park

of the campaign. Crucial and unexpected home defeats to West Bromwich Albion and Bolton in the final run-in cost them dearly, and sixth was what they had to settle for. It was a season also notable for a change in the offside law,

Hughie Gallacher

brought about primarily by the defensive tactics employed by United defenders Hampson, Hudspeth and McCracken who had perfected the art of catching opposition forwards offside. The following season, United spent a club-record fee

of £6,500 in bringing Hughie Gallacher to Tyneside from Airdrie. It was a landmark deal and he scored 15 goals in his first nine games, going on to hit 143 in 174 during his five seasons at Gallowgate. The League Championship title landed on Tyneside for the fourth time in April 1927. The Magpies were only tenth in November, but hit the number one spot in mid-January and were only to relinquish it twice for the remainder of the campaign as they battled with Huddersfield Town for the top prize in English football. The diminutive Gallacher, the club captain, scored a record 39 goals, with the likes of Seymour, Hudspeth and McDonald all playing prominent roles. United started the following season, 1927/28, like a house on fire and were second as Christmas approached. An eleven-game winless run followed and

Stan Seymour

in all, a fairly exciting and successful period for the Geordies. In 1930 (at the end of the 1929/30 season) the unthinkable happened – Gallacher was sold to Chelsea and United had appointed their first manager, Andy Cunningham (formally in post in January 1930).

Premier League Landmarks
IT'S A RECORD

Records are always there to be broken but, as at the end of the 2014/15 season, here are some of the most interesting Newcastle United and Premier League Top 10s.

NEWCASTLE UNITED RECORDS

Premier League Appearances

1. Shay Given — 354
2. Alan Shearer — 303
3. Shola Ameobi — 294
4. Rob Lee — 267
5. Nobby Solano — 230
6. Gary Speed — 213
7. Aaron Hughes — 205
8. Kieron Dyer — 190
9. Fabricio Coloccini — 185
10. Steven Taylor — 184

League Goals

1. Jackie Milburn — 177
2. Alan Shearer — 148
3. Len White — 142
4. Hughie Gallacher — 133
5. Peter Beardsley — 108
6. Tom McDonald — 100
7. Malcolm Macdonald — 95
8. Bobby Mitchell — 95
9. Neil Harris — 87
10. George Robledo — 82
10. Bryan Robson — 82

European Goal Scorers

1. Alan Shearer — 30
2. Shola Ameobi — 15
3. Craig Bellamy — 11
4. Wyn Davies — 10
5. Bryan Robson — 9
6. Tino Asprilla — 9
7. Nobby Solano — 7
8. Obafemi Martins — 6
9. Jimmy Scott — 5
10. Kieron Dyer — 5

Premier League Goals

1. Alan Shearer — 148
2. Peter Beardsley — 46
3. Andy Cole — 43
4. Shola Ameobi — 43
5. Les Ferdinand — 41
6. Nobby Solano — 37
7. Papiss Cisse — 34
8. Rob Lee — 34
9. Gary Speed — 29
10. Demba Ba — 29

FA Cup Goals

1. Jackie Milburn — 23
2. Alan Shearer — 21
3. Bobby Mitchell — 18
4. Bill Appleyard — 16
5. Albert Shepherd — 16
6. Neil Harris — 14
7. James Howie — 14
8. Malcolm Macdonald — 14
9. John Rutherford — 14
10. Tom McDonald — 13

PREMIER LEAGUE RECORDS

Appearances

1. Ryan Giggs — 632
2. Frank Lampard — 609
3. David James — 572
4. Gareth Barry — 562
5. Gary Speed — 534
6. Emile Heskey — 516
7. Mark Schwarzer — 514
8. Jamie Carragher — 508
9. Phil Neville — 505
10. Steven Gerrard — 504

Career Goals

1. Alan Shearer — 206
2. Jackie Milburn — 200
3. Len White — 153
4. Hughie Gallacher — 143
5. Malcolm Macdonald — 121
6. Peter Beardsley — 119
7. Bobby Mitchell — 113
8. Tom McDonald — 113
9. Neil Harris — 101
10. Bryan Robson — 97

League Cup Goals

1. Malcolm Macdonald — 12
2. Shola Ameobi — 8
3. Andy Cole — 8
4. Alan Shearer — 7
5. Alan Gowling — 7
6. Gavin Peacock — 5
7. Peter Beardsley — 4
8. Craig Bellamy — 4
9. Micky Burns — 4
10. Paul Cannell — 4

Goals

1. Alan Shearer — 260
2. Andy Cole — 187
3. Wayne Rooney — 185
4. Frank Lampard — 177
5. Thierry Henry — 175
6. Robbie Fowler — 163
7. Michael Owen — 150
8. Les Ferdinand — 149
9. Teddy Sheringham — 146
10. Robin van Persie — 144

Competition: Win a Signed Shirt

Answer the following question correctly and you could be in with the chance of winning a 2015/16 Newcastle United shirt, signed by some of your favourite players.

Question:

How many times have Newcastle United won the FA Cup?

Send your entry, along with your name, current address and daytime telephone number to:
competition@nufc.co.uk by 31 January 2016

The first correct entry picked at random will be the winner.
The judge's decision is final. Full terms and conditions apply
– please see below.

TERMS AND CONDITIONS

2015 Newcastle United Annual Signed Shirt Competition

ENTRY

Newcastle United Limited ("NU") (whose registered office is Newcastle United Limited, Newcastle United, St. James' Park, Newcastle upon Tyne, NE1 4ST) is the promoter of the 2016 Newcastle United Annual Signed Shirt Competition prize draw (the "Prize Draw").

By entering the Prize Draw entrants agree to be bound by these terms and conditions ("Conditions") and confirm that all information submitted is true, accurate and complete. NU reserves the right to verify the eligibility of any and all entrants and may, in its sole discretion, disqualify any entrant that fails to satisfy the eligibility requirements. Entrants shall at all times act in good faith towards NU and the Prize Draw.

Employees of NU or any of its associated companies or subsidiaries (and their families) are excluded from entering the Prize Draw.

Entry into the Prize Draw is free (except for any standard cost of postage) and on the basis of one entry per person.

In order to enter the Prize Draw and to be considered for the Prize, entrants must correctly answer the question posed and submit their entries to NU by email to competition@nufc.co.uk. Entrants must also give their full name, current address and a daytime telephone number in order to make a valid entry.

The Prize Draw will close at 12:00 GMT on Sunday 31 January 2016 (the "Closing Date") and any entries received after the Closing Date will not be entered into the Prize Draw. The Prize Draw will take place as soon as reasonably practicable following the Closing Date.

PRIZE

Subject to paragraph 8, the prize will consist of one Newcastle United shirt for Season 2015/16 signed by at least 15 current members of the Newcastle United first team squad (the "Prize"). NU will not enter into any correspondence as to which NU player(s) signs the Prize. The cost of postage of the Prize to the Winner will be borne by NU.

The Prize is non-transferable and there is no cash alternative.

WINNER

The winner will be selected at random from all valid entries received on or before the Closing Date (the "Winner").

Only the Winner of the Prize Draw will receive notification from NU. The Winner will be notified by email as soon as practicable after the Closing Date. Following the draw, the Prize will be posted to the Winner at the address submitted in the Winner's entry.

The Winner (or the Winner's parent or guardian if the Winner is under 16 years of age) will be required to give their consent to the following: (i) for the Winner's name to be disclosed to any person requesting that NU confirms the identity of the Winner; and (ii) for the Winner's name and/or photograph to be published for promotional purposes.

If NU cannot successfully contact the Winner within a reasonable length of time, or if the Winner is unable or unwilling to accept the Prize, or if the Winner does not meet the eligibility requirements, or if the Winner (or the parent or guardian of the Winner if the Winner is under 16 years of age) does

not provide the consent requested at paragraph 12 above.

Subsequent draws will take place until a new winner is found who is able, willing and eligible to accept the Prize and provide the necessary consents. This new winner shall be deemed to be the Winner for the purposes of these Conditions.

Subject to paragraphs 12 and 13 above, details of the Winner will be made available to the public upon request from Newcastle United Limited, Newcastle United, St. James' Park, Newcastle upon Tyne, NE1 4ST two weeks after the Closing Date (subject to data protection legislation).

GENERAL

NU reserves the right to cancel or amend the Prize Draw or these Conditions without notice when reasonably necessary for the purpose of administering the Prize Draw.

The Prize Draw, together with these Conditions, is governed by the laws of England and Wales and shall be subject to the exclusive jurisdiction of the English courts.

43

Newcastle United in the Community

Family football engages families from the local community in education and physical activity with the aim of enhancing knowledge of health and wellbeing, and promoting lifelong participation in exercise. All course participants came together at St James' Park to celebrate their achievements and take part in a range of fun activities where Sammy Ameobi and Jack Colback handed out their certificates and awards.

As part of the Foundation's Family Learning programme a six-week football and maths course took place at Carr Hill Primary school in Gateshead. The course helped parents and children understand the current maths curriculum in order to allow them to complete work at home. Participants were delighted to welcome Vurnon Anita and Emmanuel Riviere who took part in numerous maths games and interacted with the participants.

Holland internationals Siem de Jong and Daryl Janmaat joined 20 children from Redheugh Boys Club at the Toon Times exhibition inside the city's Discovery Museum. The Dutch duo were given a history lesson by Newcastle United Foundation staff and the children as a way of introducing both players to the football club and showing them what it means to pull on the famous black and white shirt.

44

Remy Cabella and Gabriel Obertan visited Newcastle School for Boys to assist pupils with their languages. French was the order of the day for the children at the school who peppered the two players with a multitude of different questions on life at St. James' Park and the French way of life. Gaby is United's most fluent English speaker amongst the Gallic contingent at St. James' Park and his bilingual skills proved very useful throughout the afternoon.

Newcastle United duo Ayoze Perez and Sammy Ameobi were guests of honour at the Tiny Lives Christmas Party at St. James' Park. The charity supports young children who have been patients in the Great North Children's Hospital within Newcastle's Royal Victoria Infirmary. Both players obliged with photographs and autographs, and brought Christmas cheer to all present.

Ryan Taylor and Mehdi Abeid went back to school with a visit to Wallsend Jubilee Primary School as part of the Foundation's Toon Times Heritage Project. Taylor and Abeid joined children in a special quiz to test them on their knowledge of all things Black and White. Participants studied the rich history of the football club and examined artefacts from the club's archives. Schemes such as this aim to use the local passion for football to encourage learning and promote healthy lifestyles that will make a real difference to the lives of children, young people and families in our region.

Operated in partnership with Northumbria University, Match Fit combines fitness, football and a nutrition programme for children aged 7-11, teaching them the good habits that all sports professionals must stick to. As part of the six-week course, children participate in hour-long theory lessons in the classroom followed by an hour of physical activity. Stocksfield Avenue Primary welcomed Ayoze Perez to a session where he assisted in the delivery of the physical activity and spoke to the children about the importance of having a healthy lifestyle.

Rob Elliot and Paul Dummett attended Studio West School in West Denton to work with students who were participating in the Premier League Enterprise Challenge. This is a national competition, where school groups generate schemes to attract different groups of people to their football club. In this year's challenge, the two players talked about their experiences of attending football matches in their youth and the importance of families attending matches, which helped the students generate their initiatives within the challenge.

Newcastle International Airport announced a historic partnership, with Newcastle United Foundation and Sunderland AFC's Foundation of Light becoming the airport's adopted charity for 2015 and 2016. The Foundations will work together to fundraise regularly in the terminal of Newcastle International Airport and have put forward a programme for staff engagement. The scheme was kicked off by Bob Moncur, Mike Williamson, Ayoze Perez along with Jim Montgomery and Jack Rodwell.

TOP TEN GOALS 2014/15

It wasn't a vintage season for goals but that doesn't mean the ten we've selected here aren't up with the best we've seen in recent years, both at St. James' Park and on the road. As ever there were plenty of crackers to choose from, including the winning goal from October's BBC Match of the Day 'Goal of the Month' poll.

GABRIEL **OBERTAN**
v Leicester City
(St. James' Park), 18/10/14

This was United's eighth league game of the season and they were still seeking their first win. The stadium erupted when French winger Gabriel Obertan, in a rich vein of form, hit the winner in the 71st minute. Papiss Cisse gained possession midway inside his own half and played it to Obertan who ran down the left channel from just over halfway, cutting across the edge of the box before hitting a right-footed shot back across Kasper Schmeichel – a real classy goal.

SAMMY **AMEOBI**
v Tottenham
(White Hart Lane), 26/10/14

The fastest second-half goal in Premier League history at just under seven seconds. Ayoze Perez and Yoan Gouffran kicked off and found Jack Colback on the edge of the centre circle. His left-foot pass down the wing released Sammy Ameobi, who galloped past Eric Dier. His first touch was to control the ball, his second to fire across Hugo Lloris into the far corner of the Park Lane End goal. Tottenham were stunned, the Magpies rejoiced!

ROLANDO **AARONS**
v Manchester City
(Etihad Stadium), 29/10/14

A flying start for United saw Ryan Taylor pinch the ball off a hesitant Fernandinho and play in Rolando Aarons who dashed into the box before clipping the ball through Willy Caballero's legs and into the far corner of the net from a tight angle. Aarons, in only his second starting appearance for the Magpies, sprinted to the touchline to celebrate with the Newcastle backroom staff who had helped him back to fitness – heartwarming stuff.

AYOZE **PEREZ**
v West Bromwich Albion
(The Hawthorns), 9/11/14

In the final minute of the first half, a lovely flowing move involving Moussa Sissoko, Sammy Ameobi, Massadio Haidara and Mehdi Abeid saw the ball played out to Remy Cabella on the edge of the box. The Frenchman in turn fed Daryl Janmaat who delivered a first time cross that an on-the-run Ayoze Perez flicked inside the far post with his heel. A finish of the highest order that deservedly won the MOTD award.

MOUSSA **SISSOKO**
v Queens Park Rangers
(St. James' Park), 22/11/14

Twelve minutes remained at Gallowgate with United still trying to end the R's stubborn resistance. Moussa Sissoko took possession in his own half before finding Sammy Ameobi on the left. Massadio Haidara took over and when he found Sissoko once again, a neat lay-off gave Ameobi the space he needed to arc a low pass into the box that coincided with Moussa's continuing run. He fired an unstoppable 12-yard shot into the corner of the Gallowgate goal – brilliant.

JACK COLBACK v Burnley (St. James' Park), 1/1/15

Jack Colback had opened his United goal scoring account with the winner against Everton four days earlier and here he netted his second goal in as many games, catching a low left-footed effort perfectly from a central point outside the penalty area after Daryl Janmaat had set him up from 25 yards. It was a sweet strike that whistled past a diving Tom Heaton and crashed into the Leazes End net off his left hand upright. Pick that one out!

REMY CABELLA v Hull City (KC Stadium), 31/1/15

The France international midfielder hit a pass between Michael Dawson and Gaston Ramirez that was intended for Ayoze Perez but was cut out by Andrew Robertson. The Scot inadvertently laid the ball back into the path of Cabella, who took three touches as he advanced unchecked on goal before hitting a swerving effort from 20 yards into the bottom left hand corner of the goal – 'a fabulous strike' according to BT Sports pundit Michael Owen.

MOUSSA **SISSOKO**
v Arsenal
(St. James' Park), 21/3/15

The Magpies were two down to the Gunners at the break and needed an early breakthrough. Right on cue Newcastle swept forward down the right wing at the Gallowgate End through Ryan Taylor. He found Remy Cabella who supplied a smart cut back for Moussa Sissoko to hammer home his third league goal of the season from near the penalty spot. David Ospina was left totally helpless, rooted to the spot.

MOUSSA **SISSOKO**
v West Ham United
(St. James' Park), 24/5/15

United needed this goal like no other given the circumstances of the day. Vurnon Anita swung a pass out to Jack Colback in the left channel, who advanced before exchanging passes with Paul Dummett. Jonas Gutierrez trotted past on the outside and took over, chipping in a cross that Moussa Sissoko met, forcing his way between Winston Reid and Aaron Cresswell and gleefully heading into the Gallowgate net from six yards out – and what a roar of approval that goal got! Phenomenal.

JONAS **GUTIERREZ**
v West Ham United
(St. James' Park), 24/5/15

The final goal of the season at Gallowgate, and what a fitting scorer it turned out to be. Emmanuel Riviere nodded Tim Krul's punt on to Papiss Cisse, who turned infield and found Jack Colback in centre midfield. He helped it on to the overlapping Jonas Gutierrez, who ran on before trying a low right-footed shot from outside the box that Carl Jenkinson unwittingly deflected past Adrian. Take that!

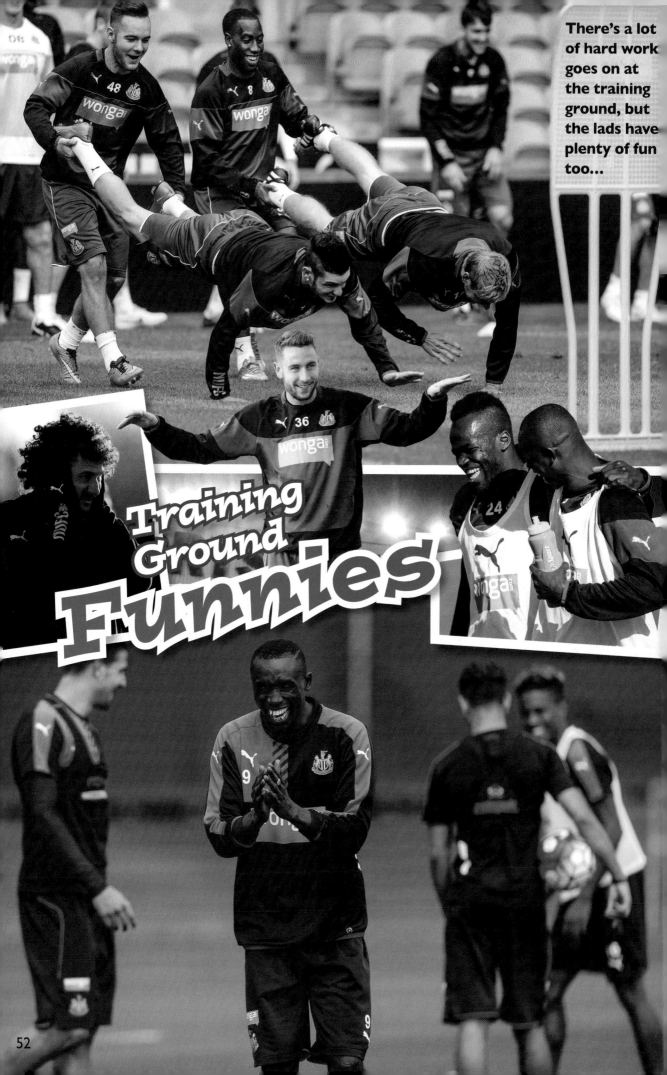

There's a lot of hard work goes on at the training ground, but the lads have plenty of fun too…

Training Ground Funnies

Where Are They Now?

The 1969 cup winners pictured at a re-union in 2009

In this special feature we take a look at the 12 men who played in both legs of the 1969 Inter Cities Fairs Cup Final, when United defeated Hungarian side Ujpest Dozsa 6 – 2 on aggregate, to see what they did after leaving Newcastle United and where they are today.

GOALKEEPER

WILLIE MCFAUL

Crucially saved a penalty in the semi-final at Rangers to help United on their way to the Final. After retiring in 1975 Willie joined the United coaching staff and took over the managerial reins in 1985 after Jack Charlton resigned. After three years in the post he returned to Northern Ireland in 1988, managing Coleraine and working with the Irish National Team, before spending five years coaching on the West Pacific island of Guam from 1999-2004. Now 72, Willie lives in retirement in Coleraine.

DEFENDERS

DAVID CRAIG

One of the best defenders in the game in the 1960s, David retired in 1975 and enjoyed a well-deserved testimonial. Born in Belfast he remained on Tyneside after his career came to an end. He ran a newspaper outlet, a heating company and, for a while, a milk business. He later became a support worker with the Edward Lloyd Trust in Newcastle helping adults with learning difficulties. Now 71 and living in Newburn, David is still involved with the Trust.

FRANK CLARK

Frank served United splendidly for 13 years before leaving for Nottingham Forest in 1975 where, incredibly, he picked up League Championship and European Cup Winners medals. After retiring he served a number of clubs, including Manchester City, in managerial roles. Later he served the League Managers Association for a lengthy period, as well as being a member of various Premier League and Football League tribunals. Now 72, Frank resides in Nottingham.

OLLIE BURTON

Ollie joined United from Norwich in 1963 and spent 10 years on Tyneside before retiring due to injury in 1973. He returned to Norfolk and did PR work for Rothmans and brewers Hurlinam, before moving into the catering business with the Sandwich Basket in Diss, Norfolk. Now 74, Ollie, remembered on Tyneside for scoring two penalties for United at Roker Park in 1967, holds an ambassadorial role at Carrow Road.

BOB MONCUR

Bob spent 14 happy years at St. James' Park, with the highlight captaining United to that Fairs Cup triumph. He later played for Sunderland before managing Carlisle, Hearts and Plymouth. An accomplished sailor, Bob also had a local taxi business, was director of Corporate Events at Aldwark Manor hotel and golf complex near York, as well as being a media pundit on local radio. Club Ambassador Bob, now 70, was appointed to the Newcastle United Board in June 2015.

MIDFIELDERS

TOMMY GIBB

Holding the United record of 171 successive games, and one of six players to play in every one of the 12 European ties, Tommy played out his career at Sunderland and Hartlepool after leaving St. James' Park in 1975. Returning to his native Scotland he managed a pub in Armadale, West Lothian before entering the haulage business. Now 71, Tommy lives in retirement in Armadale.

JIMMY SCOTT

Only with United for a short time, Scot Jimmy scored United's first European goal against Feyenoord, and also scored in the semi-final and final. Following a brief spell with Crystal Palace he moved back to his native Scotland, sadly breaking his leg whilst playing for Hamilton. He then teamed up with his brother to run the Hurlet pub (then Aitken's Bar) in Falkirk until his retirement in 2008. Now aged 75, he lives in Falkirk.

BEN ARENTOFT

Benny, now 73, was one of United's earliest foreign imports who joined United from Morton and scored in the second leg of the Fairs Cup Final in Budapest. He later played for Blackburn before securing a number of coaching positions in his native Denmark. An educated man, he was then employed as a senior manager in day-care services by Copenhagen City Council. Benny also dabbled in art dealing and accountancy before retiring to live in Stenlose, near Copenhagen.

JACKIE SINCLAIR

Sadly no longer with us, Scotsman Jackie scored the goal that sealed victory over Rangers in the Fairs Cup semi-final. Moving on to Sheffield Wednesday soon after, Jackie played out his career with Dunfermline and Stenhousemuir. He was later employed by the National Coal Board at Solsgirth pit, worked at Stirling University and was Dunfermline Golf Club's steward before his untimely death from cancer in September 2010 aged 67.

STRIKERS

BRYAN 'POP' ROBSON

Bryan scored on his United debut and teamed up superbly with Wyn Davies to terrorise European defences during the Fairs Cup run. He went on to enjoy success at West Ham and Sunderland, but unfortunately missed both those teams' Wembley cup wins. A fine golfer, Bryan ran a newsagency on Tyneside before concentrating on coaching and scouting, most notably as Sunderland's chief scout until May 2013. Now 70, Pop lives in retirement in Hexham.

WYN DAVIES

Wyn 'the leap' Davies wasn't a prolific scorer, but his contribution to the side during his five years on Tyneside was immense. He was the club's top scorer in Europe until he was overtaken by Alan Shearer some 35 years on. He later played for both Manchester clubs with distinction, one of a handful of men to do so, before settling in Bolton after retiring from the game and working for Warburton's bakery. Now 73, he still lives in Bolton.

ALAN FOGGON

Local lad Alan was on the fringe of the United first team in 1969 and put his name in the history books in Setubal, becoming the club's youngest ever European goalscorer at just 19 years and 17 days. A goal-scoring substitute in Budapest, Alan also played for Sunderland and Middlesbrough during his 13-year career. After football, Foggon became a publican in Jarrow and Spennymoor and also worked for a security firm on Tyneside. Aged 65 he now lives in Hebburn.

For the record, there were 10 other players who played in some of the earlier round matches, namely Geoff Allen, Albert Bennett, John Craggs, Keith Dyson, Dave Elliott, Ron Guthrie, Arthur Horsfield, Jim Iley, John McNamee and Graham Winstanley.

A TO Z OF NEWCASTLE UNITED

A

Albert – Who can ever forget Philippe's chip over Peter Schmeichel in 1996.

B

Bobby Robson – A true great of the game.

C

Cup Kings – United won the FA Cup three times at Wembley in the 1950s.

D

Derby matches – You can't beat a North-East derby! United lead Sunderland by 53 to 51 wins.

E

Edwardian Era – United were the top team of the era winning the League three

times and the FA Cup once, as well as finishing in the top four six times and being beaten Cup finalists on four occasions, narrowly missing out the famed 'double'.

F

Fulham – United's 6 – 0 defeat of the Cottagers is the record winning margin in an FA Cup Semi Final.

G

Gallacher – United's talismanic captain of the 1926/27 Championship winning side. Hughie scored 39 goals in that memorable season.

H

Harvey – The great Joe Harvey who won honours as both player and manager at St. James' Park.

I

Inter-Cities Fairs Cup – the European Trophy United won in Budapest in 1969.

J

Janmaat – Daryl made 37 league appearances for United in 2014/15, more than any other player.

K

Kingsley – Matt was United's first capped England player in 1901.

L

Lawrence – goalkeeper Jim has played 496 games for United, more than any other player.

M

McCracken, McWilliam, McMichael and all the other great players down the years to have the 'Mc' name.

N

Number 9 – The famous Newcastle United Number 9 shirt worn by Milburn, Macdonald and Shearer to name but three Geordie legends.

O

Opposition – United have faced 181 different teams in their history, the most recent being Morecambe in 2013.

P

Promotion – United have won promotion to the top flight on six occasions, 1897/98, 1947/48, 1964/65, 1983/84, 1992/93 and 2009/10.

Q

Quickest send-off – that unfortunate record belongs to Jimmy Smith, after only 53 seconds in a Texaco Cup game against Birmingham in 1973.

R

Rutherford – Jack is United's youngest ever goal scorer, netting against Bolton in 1902 aged just 17 years, 4 months and 21 days.

S

St. James' Park – Home to Newcastle United Football Club since 1892.

T

Toon – The Geordie word for our fantastic city of Newcastle upon Tyne.

U

Urwin – Tom is the only player with a surname beginning with U to play for United (1924-30).

V

Veitch – Colin, an Edwardian master and true great of the game, also excelled off the pitch in a number of roles.

W

Wilson – the most popular name in United's playing history. 12 Wilsons have played for the club, with Terry the last one in 1992.

X

X-Rated – some of the tackles made by rugged defenders down the years at St. James' Park.

Y

Youth Cup – United have won the competition twice, in 1962 and 1985 (below).

Z

Zico – United's very own Mick Martin.

Did You Know?

United have a great history but there are numerous miscellaneous facts you may not be aware of. Here are just a few.

JANUARY

1893

Newcastle United's first FA Cup match, a First Round loss at home to Middlesbrough.

1946

United play their first 'competitive' fixture after World War Two, a 4 – 2 home win over Barnsley in the FA Cup in front of 60,284. For the only time in the competition's history, third round ties are played over two-legs and United crash out after losing 3 – 0 at Oakwell.

1953

Fog causes the abandonment of United's Third Round FA Cup tie with Swansea at St. James' Park after only eight minutes and 63,499 fans go home early! United win 3 – 0 four days later with another 61,064 fans present. That victory set a then FA Cup record of 16 ties unbeaten.

1989

United play their fourth FA Cup third round tie against Watford, losing the third replay 1 – 0 at Vicarage Road, United's longest tie on record.

1999

Peter Beardsley has his Testimonial at St. James' Park with a full house of 36,733 present to see a United XI take on Glasgow Celtic, the Scots winning 3 – 1.

2008

United are watched by the largest crowd to see them play in a League  fixture, with 75,965 at Manchester United.

FEBRUARY

1896

United start their home game with Burton with only 8 players, but win 4 – 0.

1923

In the fixture at Cardiff, United's  full-backs of Bill McCracken (40) and Billy Hampson (38), with keeper Sandy Mutch (38) form United's oldest defensive formation.

1956

United take part in the Football League's first floodlit game, a 2 – 0 win at Portsmouth, Bill Curry having the distinction of scoring the first Football League goal under the lights.

1965

United appear on BBC Match of the Day for the first time, losing 2 – 1 at Orient.

1998

For the first time in their history United select a starting XI who are all International capped players.

MARCH

1894

Newcastle United are awarded their first penalty, scored by Harry Jeffrey against Walsall Town Swifts.

1901

First International game played at St. James' Park, England v Wales.

1963

United play at Bradford in a third round FA Cup tie, the match having been postponed a record 12 times throughout January and February.

APRIL

1910

Albert Shepherd became the first player to take and score a penalty in an FA Cup final.

1915

Tommy Goodwill scores for United in the final League game before World War One. He would later be killed in action.

1924

The FA Cup Final was the first time the match had been declared 'an all-ticket' occasion.

1932

HRH Prince of Wales, later King Edward VIII, watches Newcastle take on Blackpool at St. James' Park, it ended 2 – 2.

1974

United meet Birmingham City for the seventh time in the same season, the most fixtures against the same club in one season.

1986

United field three different goalkeepers (Thomas, Hedworth and Beardsley) at West Ham, eventually losing 8 – 1.

MAY

1904

United play their first match on foreign soil, a 6 – 1 exhibition game win against a Copenhagen XI in Denmark.

1944

The Football League North encounter with Darlington lasted a record 143 minutes, United's longest ever game. It also counted as a Tyne-Tees-Wear Cup Final with the teams playing on until someone scored, Jackie Milburn doing so in the 143rd minute!

1948

United's last home game of the season creates a record average attendance of over 56,000.

1967

Jackie Milburn has his Testimonial at St. James' Park with 45,404 present to see a United and Sunderland Select XI take on an International XI.

1984

United draw 2 – 2 with Liverpool in a farewell game for Kevin Keegan at St. James' Park, he disappears into the night in a helicopter from the centre circle.

2006

Shay Given ends the season as an ever-present in the League for the fourth time, a club record.

A crowd of 52,275 pack St. James' Park to bid farewell to Alan Shearer in a televised spectacular against Glasgow Celtic.

2010

United win 1 - 0 at QPR to reach 102 points – a club record. It is also Newcastle's 30th league win of the season, another record.

JUNE

1940

United play two wartime first-team fixtures on the same day, against Leeds and Bradford City.

1969

United play their 59th senior game of the season, a club record.

1995

Peter Beardsley becomes the first Newcastle United player ever to feature in the Queen's Honours List, being awarded an MBE.

1996

St. James' Park hosts the Euro 96 Finals fixture between France and Bulgaria, one of three games at the stadium.

AUGUST

1894

United formally change their colours from red and white to black and white.

SEPTEMBER

1892

The newly formed Newcastle United play their first game at St. James' Park, a 1 – 0 friendly defeat to Glasgow Celtic.

1893

United's club colours in their first season in the Football League were red and white.

1894

United play in their new black and white shirts in the League for the first time, an away fixture at Darwen.

2009

In the League Cup tie at Peterborough, United fielded their youngest ever line-up for a first team game, the average age being 21 years and 51 days.

OCTOBER

1961

Bobby Mitchell has his Testimonial at St. James' Park with 40,993 present to see a United XI lose 3 – 2 to a Bobby Mitchell XI.

NOVEMBER

1881

Stanley FC formed in Byker.

DECEMBER

1892

East End change their name to Newcastle United.

1949

Brothers George and Ted Robledo play in the same line-up for the first time against Aston Villa at Villa Park.

GOING FOR GOAL

There's nothing quite like scoring a goal! The players love it and the fans get hugely emotional too. Here we feature some of the most joyous goal celebrations from the 2014/15 season.

60

61

Quiz Answers

GOING FOR GOAL p16

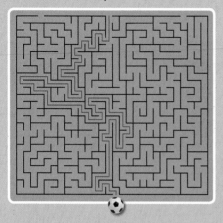

NUFC MATHS CHALLENGE p17

A. (2010) ÷ (30) - (22) = (45)   **Aleksandar Mitrovic**
B. (7) + (4) x (2) = (22)   **Daryl Janmaat**
C. (8) x (5) ÷ (20) = (2)   **Fabricio Coloccini**
D. (206) - (80) ÷ (9) = (14)   **Jack Colback**
E. (40) x (3) ÷ (12) = (10)   **Siem De Jong**

THREE OF A KIND p20

1. Chelsea, Crystal Palace, Charlton
2. Arsenal, Southampton and Tottenham
3. Alan Shearer, Peter Beardsley, Andy Cole
4. Shay Given, Aaron Hughes, Nikos Dabizas
5. Charles N'Zogbia, Kevin Nolan, Alan Neilson
6. West Brom, Tottenham and Hull
7. Shearer, Solano and Speed

BONUS ANSWERS p20

1. Arsenal, Tottenham, Chelsea
2. N'Zogbia, Given, Solano
3. Shearer, Solano, N'Zogbia

QUIZ 1 p21

1. Gabriel Obertan (v Gillingham)
2. Leicester City
3. Manchester City
4. Crystal Palace, Everton, Burnley, Hull
5. Mike Williamson
6. 8
7. Davide Santon
8. Sunderland and Manchester City
9. Lubo Satka and Callum Roberts
10. Burnley (New Year's Day)

QUIZ 2 p21

1. Won the Inter Cities Fairs Cup
2. Tottenham
3. QPR
4. Stan Seymour
5. Tottenham
6. Willie McFaul
7. Blue (Sheffield Wednesday had no change kit!)
8. Real Madrid
9. Benfica
10. Diego Gavilan

CROSSWORD p23

SPOT THE DIFFERENCE p24

THE NAME GAME p25

Peter Lovenkrands	Denmark	Alessandro Pistone	Italy
Cheik Tiote	Ivory Coast	Hugo Viana	Portugal
Jonas Gutierrez	Argentina	Philippe Albert	Belgium
Tino Asprilla	Columbia	Clarence Acuna	Chile
Emre	Turkey	Andreas Andersson	Sweden
Nobby Solano	Peru	Diego Gavilan	Paraguay
Mark Hottiger	Switzerland	Temuri Ketsbaia	Georgia
Nikos Dabizas	Greece	Didi Hamann	Germany
Pavel Srnicek	Czech Republic	Geremi	Cameroon
Cacapa	Brazil	Obafemi Martins	Nigeria

SPOT THE BALL p38

SPOT THE BALL p38

WORDSEARCH p39

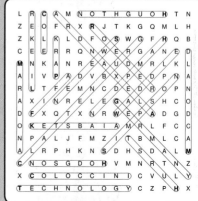